My Farmer, My Customer

Acres U.S.A.

Testimonials

Praise For Marty Travis and the Spence Farm

This is a great book—authentic, inspirational, practical. Whether you are an aspiring farmer (or even one that knows the ropes), a chef, a restaurateur, a food-service provider or just someone with an appetite and curiosity for understanding how to be a part of the good food system, you'll find richness in these candid, personal pages from one of the most visionary farmers I know."

Rick Bayless
Chef-Owner of Chicago's Frontera Grill and host of Public Television's "Mexico: One Plate at a Time".

In 2016, Marty changed my life by inviting me into his world and showing me a different way of farming. "Sustainability" is pivotal for not just chefs like myself, but for the human race. We must continue to educate people and young farmers about the importance of sustainability. Marty's way of farming will really change the world.

Justin Ferguson
Executive Chef / Owner
BRQ Restaurant / Bacon & Fig Events

Marty Travis is so full of knowledge about sustainable farming, but more importantly to me is that he has a pure love of the craft that farming truly is. He takes care and pride in every step with respect for the land and what it can give us. I have been fortunate over the years to get to learn from Marty in a hands-on way at Spence Farm. It's been an experience he and his family have been kind enough to share with so many chefs, to help open our eyes to another side of the food system. Marty is amazing for his inspiration and guidance to now be shared with even more of the world.

Stephanie Izard

Executive Chef/Owner Girl and the Goat, Little Goat, and Duck Duck Goat, James Beard Award Winner, 2013

Marty Travis is my favorite person in this crazy industry we exist in, and I am a better chef for knowing him.

Brett Coolidge

Chef, Hopleaf Restaurant

Marty and his family truly live the term, "farm to table". When I was first introduced to the Travis, it was their American Guinea hogs that caught my eye, as they were something I had never worked with before. The insanely marbled flesh reminded me of something similar to Kobe or Wagyu beef with a buttery texture and an aged nutty flavor. I was hooked ...

The introduction of a new breed of pig was just the beginning of what would begin a long and exciting relationship of weekly visits to our hotel, bringing produce that was not only the freshest of the season's peak, but had a story and a name (usually several family members names) of the farm it came from. The introduction of true local products flooded our hotel, which provided sustainable products year-round, ranging from eggs and milled corn for our breakfast service, to half sides of beef we would grind for our house burgers, and tomatoes and peppers we would cook down for a years supply of hot sauce. Marty and his co-op of farmers offered so much knowledge and passion about their cultivated crops, it was hard not to become protective of the products and their uses. Over the years, I have been fortunate to see the list of farmers and ingredients grow week over week anticipating his Friday email listing all that was available and eagerly submitting my request hoping that I wasn't too late to secure my cases of fresh treasures that would undoubtedly sell out if I waited too long.

The mantra at the hotel became, "We believe you should know where your food comes from, who grew it and what is in it," which is printed on each seasons menu and still holds true to this day.

Joshua Hasho

Executive Chef, Omni Hotels

This engaging and informative book is not only an indispensable toolkit for the farmer or chef seeking a template for building a sustainable food system through innovation, inclusion and creative thinking, it's also for anyone interested in delving into a deeply personal story packed with practical advice about how one small family farm transformed struggle into triumph. They did it by creating a dynamic network of passionate individuals who work together in the spirit of collaboration, guided by the belief that if we support one another, the small can become a mighty, invincible force for good.

Jody Eddy

Author of the upcoming "Elysian Kitchens: Recipes and Stories From Monasteries, Mosques, Temples and Synagogues Around the World", published by W.W. Norton in 2020 and "The Chaat Express", published by Clarkson Potter in 2020.

My Farmer, My Customer

Acres U.S.A.
P.O. Box 1690
Greeley, Colorado 80632 U.S.A.
970-392-4464
info@acresusa.com • www.acresusa.com
ecofarmingdaily.com • events.acresusa.com

Printed in the United States of America

Cover and interior design by Carl Chiocca; special thanks to Afton Pospisilova.

Front cover photography used with permission from Matt Wechsler.
All photos inside used with permission.

Publisher's Cataloging-in-Publication Data

Names: Travis, Marty, author.
Title: My farm, my customer : uncovering what it takes to produce the food we want to eat / Marty Travis.
Description: Includes bibliographical references, index, tables, and illustrations. | Greeley, CO: Acres U.S.A., 2020.
Identifiers: ISBN 978-1-60173-154-8 (Softcover) | 978-1-60173-155-5 (ebook)
Subjects: LCSH Family Farms -- Management | Sustainable Agriculture | Local Foods | Family Farms -- Economic Aspects | Farmers -- Illinois -- Biography | BISAC TECHNOLOGY & ENGINEERING / Agriculture / Organic | BUSINESS & ECONOMICS / Marketing / Direct
Classification: LCC S561 .T73 2020 | DDC 630/.68

My Farmer, My Customer

Building Business and Community Through Farming Healthy Food

By Marty Travis *with Gary Reding*

Acres U.S.A.
Greeley, Colorado

Table of Contents

Preface

Dear Reader,

    I did not start out to be a farmer. While we had a family farm, I knew from an early age I wanted to be a woodworker. And that is what I became. Somewhere after thirty-plus years of building furniture for wonderful people all over the world, I had a crossroads moment. At that moment my wife, Kris, asked, "If you weren't able to do woodworking any longer, what would you do?" I said, "Well, we have this cute little farm; maybe we should do something with it."

    That is where this story of my farming life began.

    There are so many questions when you begin a new adventure; so much to learn, so much to discover. We don't even know what we don't know! So, part of the exercise in writing this book revolves around the sharing of experiences—sharing how we have learned to listen intently, learn quickly, and fail better. And after getting over the hump, I have all of this stuff in my head that needs to be shared. I hear so many folks who want to follow their dream and live on the land and farm! Where do we begin?

    Let me first begin by saying this: the thoughts and information I share in these pages are my experiences, and they encapsulate my belief in what is true for me. Please understand that I do not profess to have all the answers, or even your answers. In my experience, the only way a system can be successful is if it's developed with consideration of the farmer/owner's intent, the environment, and a whole number of factors. It is important for me to say this so you don't think I am some know-it-all. I am sharing these experiences with you, the reader, and am admitting my vulnerability in doing so.

My hope and desire for this information is to be helpful, inspiring, empowering, and real. Sometimes I feel like a cheerleader, encouraging folks to just try it, keep going, and keep moving forward. Sometimes all any of us need is someone to believe in us, to believe we can do it. We are lucky in that we had a number of friends, family, and neighbors who encouraged and inspired us. For that, we are truly grateful.

My other hope for this book is that it becomes a book that listens. I know that sounds nearly impossible in a physical sense. But what I mean is that my intention was to write this in such a way that you and I can have a conversation. That we can understand and collaborate about the questions, the fear, the joy, and all of the other feelings that surface when we are open to a new possibility. That we can hear each other as you read this and know that not only am I listening, but that I am invested in your success. So read on. There is much to share.

Sincerely,
Marty Travis

Foreword

In the summer of 2013, my wife and I embarked on a project that, three years later, would become the feature-length documentary *Sustainable*. The title of the film came to us right away, but the content did not. We knew we wanted to define what it meant to have a sustainable food system, but how would we tell that story, and who were our characters?

Living in Chicago, we knew we had to find Midwest farmers with whom we could visit in a matter of hours, and we knew who to ask— Chef Rick Bayless. Rick started the Green City Market in the 1990s and pioneered the local food movement in Chicago. His answer was immediate: "You have to visit Spence Farm."

So, on October 8, 2013, we drove down to Spence Farm to do some filming. We honestly thought this would be the only time we would go down there and figured it would be a three-minute segment in the whole film. We even planned two other stops at nearby farms, but what was supposed to be a small two-hour thing turned into a discovery of so much more. It was a real farm—like one you would see in a movie—with hundreds of crop varieties, pastured heritage livestock, foraging chickens and ducks, an old schoolhouse, red barns, hoop houses, forty acres of woods, and amber waves of grain. But more interesting than the land itself was the farmer.

Marty Travis is one of those people you never forget—genuine and humble with an amazing spirit for life. He is a glass-half-full type of guy and a deep thinker. Marty is open minded—what seems like a good idea may develop based on new information. Everything he does has intention. He only works with people he likes—a policy everyone should adopt. He is sincere, honest, hardworking, and diligent. Marty has built a local food distribution enterprise that brings value to his community through handshakes and personal relationships. He is a perfect example of a social entrepreneur.

Needless to say, we quickly realized Marty was our story. Over the course of the next two years, we visited Spence Farm roughly twenty times to capture the incredible work being done there. We learned about American Guinea Hogs, Einkorn wheat, Iroquois white corn, Dexter cows, crop rotations, harvesting, beekeeping, soil amending, composting, maple syrup, native prairieland, and more. Much of that amazing information never made it into the film, but it is in this book.

Perhaps the most amazing story to me, though, is the story of the farm and how it transitioned. My wife and I had convinced ourselves that Marty must be this longtime farmer who learned all this incredible knowledge through his ancestry. While Marty's love of the land and love of farming certainly comes from his heritage, the rest of the story is quite different. Marty built Shaker reproduction furniture for thirty-five years. In that time, he saw the farm change hands from his family, to a conventional farmer, and then back to his family. So Marty did not inherit a diverse farm with productive, organic soil—he had to figure out how to transition the land on his own. The fact that he did that, acre by acre, without taking shortcuts, and now has an incredibly diverse farm with healthy soil, speaks volumes about who he is as a person.

Marty is not just a farmer to me; he is a mentor, on and off the soil. He didn't just teach me about biodiversity; he taught me to love the unknown—Blue Hopi baby corn, purple Brussel sprouts, Brazilian church bell peppers, and hundreds of other weird and interesting varieties. He inspired me to plant my own heirloom varieties and to trust my instincts in gardening. More than that, he taught me the importance in having a passion for what I do. I spent thirteen years working for clients before producing *Sustainable*. Since then, I've transitioned to only working for people I like and only doing work I enjoy. I love what I do now, and I have Marty to thank for guiding me in this direction.

Matt Wechsler
Director, *Sustainable*

Spence Farm
*was an incredible
place to explore
and to experience.*

CHAPTER 1

Where to Begin? Farm Dreams

This is where it all began. I grew up spending a lot of time on my grandparents' 160-acre farm, Spence Farm. It was an incredible place to explore and to experience. It had barns and buildings of all sorts. There was the sheep barn, the cow barn, a milk house, smoke house, butcher shed, equipment shed, syrup house, and blacksmith shop, to name a few. It had a wood lot that seemed so big! The woods were the private hideaway where you could go and sit and watch birds, squirrels, or falling leaves. Time stood still there. We picked strawberries, walked fields of soybeans, and pulled weeds in the rows, and I learned what I could at the age of twelve.

That winter my grandfather passed away. One thing I remember him telling me the summer before was to learn as much as possible about lots of things and not just a lot about one thing. It is kind of like the saying, "Be a jack of all trades and master of none!" That one piece of advice really stuck with me. I have missed him and could sure have used a lot of his sage advice as we worked to build this farm into one in which I am sure he would have been proud.

Our family farm was settled in October of 1830 by my fourth great-grandfather, Valentine Martin Darnall, who had purchased the land from the government for $1.25 per acre. He and his wife and four young children came here from Kentucky. They erected a small cabin and endured one of the worst winters on record their first year. We still have a few relics from Valentine; they are mementos that help us to remember that we don't have it so bad!

The farm passed down through the generations, and after my grandfather's passing it went through another transition. In 1981 my grandmother moved to town and sold the homestead and the small field to the north of the house to a neighboring farmer. She retained the other 140 acres. After another eighteen years, that neighboring farmer sold the homestead back to my grandmother and moved their family back to their own family's homestead. So, in the spring of 1999, I moved back to Grandma's house.

I was still a woodworker then. I built reproduction Shaker furniture for people all over the world. It was fun and rewarding work to be able to replicate original Shaker pieces for clients such as Macy's, the Smithsonian Museum gift shop, Chicago executive buildings, and more. All through that time, I realized I never produced anything that anyone really needed. Not that I believed what I was doing wasn't important; I just realized that I was working for clients that had a lot of disposable income to purchase extracurricular items.

Sometime in the very early 2000s, Kris asked me that important and pivotal question: "What would you do if you couldn't do woodworking any longer?" It wasn't that things weren't going along well enough making furniture. There were plenty of orders, a lot of trips to the East Coast, and lots of inspiration from pieces in museums and private collections. It was something that was a bit nagging from living on the land. What were WE going to do with it? How were we going to better it? Answering that question became an opportunity for us to work together along with our son, Will. Giving credit where credit is due, Kris was the one with the inspiration from the beginning. It is quite probable that none of this story would have happened if it weren't for her vision.

The three of us began to imagine what was possible. Where do we begin? What should we grow? Where do we sell it? How much money can we make? Can we make enough to live on? How do we make it work for all of us?

Those are really important questions to ask, and they often are hard questions to find the right answers to. We still had the income from woodworking, as I didn't quit cold turkey. But if we were going to do it, we had to figure it out. At that point, almost all the farmland around us was in conventional GMO corn and soybeans. Well, we didn't want to do that. We didn't have any equipment, nor any real working knowledge of growing large-scale agricultural crops. We had gardened and knew how to do that. But who buys that? How can you make a living on a garden?

About that time, we had an older cousin with twenty-six acres of woodland that was covered in the early spring with wild ramps— *Allium triccocum*, a wild, native onion species. In his woodland they were pervasive, if not invasive. They were literally as thick as grass from mid-March through the end of April. Ramp leaves look a lot like Lily of the Valley, except they grow in clumps. They have this incredible oniony, garlicky smell, especially when you step on them, which is not hard to do when they were everywhere! Our cousin wasn't that excited about them, as he felt they were crowding out some of the other native wildflowers. So we began researching and learning about ramps. We discovered there were ramp festivals in the Appalachians.

We explored the possibility of providing ramps to the ramp festivals, as many of the local ramp populations were dwindling due to over-harvesting. We finally found a company, Earthy Delights, in Lansing, Michigan, that would take all we could dig, clean. and transport.

We would commence harvesting as soon as the plants began emerging in March. We would hand-dig the largest plants, leaving the smaller ones to grow and repopulate the area. We harvested nearly 1,000 pounds per week. We made the delivery trip once per week, driving from our farm to Lansing in about five hours. The first week was the hardest! We had loaded the van the night before so we could get an early start. Wow, what a stench upon opening the van door that next morning! We made it, received payment upon delivery, and came back ready for more.

After that first season we were approached by another company that wanted to order ramps, too. Upon further research, we discovered that both these companies were selling ramps to a lot of the Chicago restaurants. During the winter leading up to our third season, we were invited by a friend to attend a Chef's Collaborative meeting in Chicago. It was a small group of the best chefs in the city. We were so green and aware of our lack of experience! After meeting them, they all asked if they could purchase our ramps. From then on we sold directly to about a half dozen restaurants.

Very quickly, word traveled throughout the chef world, and we had calls from another dozen restaurants asking if we would sell to them as well. Soon we had an opportunity in our laps. Nearing the end of the ramp season, nearly every chef asked what else we could provide to them. We had nothing to sell, but we knew we could grow whatever they were looking for, and that is how we really began to grow.

So, let's stop here and evaluate our situation, knowing what we know today. One of the questions we tend to ask new farmers today is, "What is your dream? Why do you want to do this? What are your core values?"

I like to look at things in an order of **outcomes**, **methods**, and **resources**. I learned this concept a long time ago from a mentor in Indiana.

OUTCOMES

What is the desired outcome? For us, it was finding an income source utilizing the resources we had in front of us. Kris had asked the question, and we talked about the farm and what we had in our laps, including the resource in our cousin's woodland: the ramps. We also wanted to follow the traditions of our family farm and honor all the history that had taken place here. Understand what you want to do. If it is just to supplement your current income, or to be able to have more family time, or to allow your kids the opportunity to learn from a farm setting, all of those are worthy outcomes. Sit down and list them.

METHODS

Next, figure out the methods you need to use to achieve those outcomes. How will you choose what to grow? How are you going to make this work? How are you going to interact with your customers or your community? How will you market and distribute your product or service? Methods are important to understand. In the beginning, we knew we wanted to grow things without chemicals. That was important to our own personal philosophy. So, we decided we wanted to focus on heirloom and native crops and heritage breed livestock. We wanted to be a part of preserving that rich, yet disappearing, heritage. We worked hard to understand how to achieve those outcomes!

RESOURCES

Finally, resources. Many people begin their thinking with resources. Sometimes we catch ourselves doing that, too. But we can't know exactly what resources to use unless we know the desired outcomes and what methods we need to get there. It's kind of like having a whole tool box full of tools but no purpose for using them.

Let's say that our goal is to replace a broken part on an implement. How are we going to do that? What methods can we use? Next, what tools or resources can we use to make the repair? We can't just use any tool; we have to have a plan of attack first. Beating things with hammers and wrenches doesn't usually bring the most favorable result!

In our case, we wanted to be able to provide chemical-free produce to the larger community. That was one of our strong desires. The methods then became the "how". How do we do that? Finally, we figured out what we had and what we needed. We also discovered whom to ask the "how" questions of. We were able to utilize folks like Seed Savers Exchange, Baker Creek Heirloom Seeds, and the American Livestock Breeds Conservancy for those answers.

One of our local resources was a couple named Roy and Ivy Mae Peterson. We discovered that they had grown produce in the 1970s and had sold it to a few grocery stores and farmers' markets. They lived about eight miles from the farm, and I called them up one day and asked if we could stop by to visit. Roy was in his late 80s. While we may not have taken so much away from the conversation in terms of answers to our "How do we do that?" questions, Roy and Ivy Mae said a couple of things that still resonate today.

First, they said they believed in us. Stop there and let that sink in. That was huge! They said that we could do it and that they would be there anytime we had questions.

Second, Roy told us, "All you are doing is selling water; it just comes in different packages!" We plant a seed and nourish it with healthy soil and (hopefully timely) rains. Then it produces the crop that we sell to be consumed; mostly water! I thought right away about the need to have the best starting seed and the best environment for those seeds so that we could harvest the best water ... encapsulated therein!

WHERE TO BEGIN?

How do I start? Do I begin just by growing something and then trying to find a market for it? Do I begin with the soil, getting livestock, or planting something? What do I do? Sound familiar? My advice is to begin with writing out your dream. What does your farm look like in your mind's eye? What is it you wish to accomplish and why? What need are you working to fulfill in your life or your family's life? Write out the plan in terms of one year, three years, and beyond. Start small! I mean it! Jumping into the deep end is for folks who know how to swim. Work toward easily managed successes and develop your market as you go. Building your business at a pace you can manage is vitally important; however, it can be very difficult.

DEFINING CONCEPTS/RULES

One of the first rules we made and continue to live by was that we were only going to work with nice people.

I can hear you now: "Oh, well, that sounds really immature!" Well, let me tell you how much easier our lives are as a result of adopting this rule! When we have farmers, chefs, or grocery stores that don't want to play nice, it makes it super easy to say, "We can't work with you."

We don't need the stress, and you don't either. There are enough people in this world who are nice, and those are the ones with whom we wish to associate. I am not into having a chef yell on the phone about some piece of dirt they found on a radish or a grocery store that complains every other week about how much we charge for such and such, without knowing what goes into planting, tending, harvesting, and then delivering of that product to them for $1.50/pound! Seek out and work with nice people from the beginning. It is much easier and way more peaceful for everyone. You are empowered to choose with whom and how you wish to work.

Next up, you need to realize that your farm enterprise is nearly 80 percent relationship building and 20 percent actual farming. I think maybe this figure comes from Joel Salatin, author and farmer extraordinaire. It is 100 percent true. Here are some points to help explain:

- Learn the art of excellent communication.
- Listen intently as your customer talks to you.
- Hear what they are saying in words and also in unspoken language.

John Ikerd, an economist and author, also says, "The greatest challenge in creating a sustainable food system is the art and science of maintaining personal relationships." I agree whole heartedly.

From the beginning, the relationship was the key to our success. Every delivery day is not necessarily a marketing day. Sometimes it is just listening to your client—in our case, the chef. What is going on in their world? How are their kids? We have had so many back-alley talks. Often we knew before anyone else that a chef was leaving the restaurant or was getting a divorce or having a child. We became a sounding board for ideas, frustrations, or successes. Having that kind of relationship is vital to our success and theirs! There are many times we don't even really discuss what we have for sale. We almost never pressure anyone to buy something. Maybe we're missing out on a sale that someone else would get, but we know in the end that we are where we need to be. Having said that, we are also hugely respectful of everyone's time. We don't believe in going on and on about some topic. Everyone is busy and has something to do. So respect that!

Chefs especially are visual characters. Besides that, we also think they were the infants and toddlers who put everything in their mouth!

Watch this sometime if you get a chance. When we bring a new item to a chef, they invariably pop it in their mouth and then ask, "What is it?" But if you think about their world and how they sell their wares, it is visual. They want to envision whatever you have to offer on a plate. So, one of the things we have done for a number of years is to bring them the veggie "porn" catalogs. You know—the Baker Creek, Seed Savers, Johnny's, and others. That way they can look through them and see what looks good. We ask them to choose some varieties that they would like to work with and ask them to give us a weekly amount they'd like to order during that season. That has worked super well. It is much easier to know what and how much your customer will buy ahead of the planting season.

This kind of relationship marketing works in the farmers' market and CSA settings, too. It seems to me that people today who are passionate about food are yearning for a connection with the producer of that food. They wish to have a real person to connect with. They want to know that someone who cares deeply about producing good, clean food is providing them or their family with sustenance. So this is a great place to begin. People need to eat. Please don't tell me, "Marty, you have the Chicago market and that is what makes your success possible!" Everyone eats! Everyone. There are so many opportunities, from schools to local groceries, restaurants, markets, neighbors, workplace take-home boxes, and on and on. We have never advertised and in the past two years we have turned down more than fifty new restaurant accounts because we can't do it all. Build a relationship with someone that is nice and that eats! Figure out what they want to eat, produce that, and then we can get on to realizing your farm dream.

Next chapter!

Ramping Up
Wild ramps are already in the forests near our home from mid-March to the end of April. They enabled us to start our farm dream.

Bugs

Spiders are just one example of the great biodiversity that has returned to Spence F. since we instituted regenerative practice

Photo Credit: Carol Richmond

CHAPTER 2

Rules of Nature —or— Nature Rules!

T here is so much we have learned when it comes to working with nature. There is also so much more to learn. Remember that one rule we established in Chapter 1 about only working with nice people? Well, this is my notice to you. Mostly, Mother Nature doesn't care about being nice. Nature is nature and we have to come to an understanding of this. Nature is beautiful, incredibly inspiring, and really something to behold! Nature is also very harsh, unrelenting, and powerful. My friend, Gary Reding, shared with us his Four Rules of Nature:

1. Everything is connected to everything.
2. Everything goes somewhere.
3. There is no free lunch.
4. Mother Nature always bats last!

So we must come to an understanding of how nature works. We need to have a healthy respect for her and we need to work on our farms in ways that encourage and develop systems for enhancing natural processes and natural communities. When we think about that first rule of nature—that everything is connected to everything—we need to look at the whole farm using that as a lens.

Organic Certification

When we began this journey, we knew that we wanted to grow all our crops without the use of pesticides, herbicides, fungicides, or chemical fertilizer. As consumers, we look for the organic label in the store to have some assurance that the food we will be eating was grown without those chemicals as well. Also, we don't want to consume genetically modified foods. The organic label is one way of coming to understand a bit more on how that food is produced. Without knowing the specific farmer, the label becomes somewhat of a default in the shopper's experience.

Applying that scenario to our farm, we felt that our potential customers wouldn't necessarily know who we were and what we stood for, at least until we got to know each other. So we became certified organic. Then, as we developed relationships with our chefs and individuals, the need for certification became almost moot. Any of our customers could visit the farm and do the walk and talk and come to trust what we said and what we did. This is not to say that certification has no place; but in our specific situation, we no longer needed it to "market" our product.

Rule #1:

Everything Is Connected

Let's start with this: Do you have land? Access to land? Let's evaluate the options.

For many aspiring farmers, access to land is a real limiting factor. How do we find it? We have worked with farmers who use their own in-town backyards, neighbors' yards, and even community garden space. In the country, finding suitable garden or field space can be just as challenging. Talk to folks. County Soil and Water District employees sometimes have ideas of people who might be amenable to a food farmer. Even renting an odd acre or more may be a way to begin. There are a few farms with odd-shaped corner fields that are becoming increasingly hard to cope with in the age of huge equipment. Sometimes they are a possibility for an alternative crop. In our community, we have had older folks who own property who are looking for a person to farm in a more sustainable manner. Food farming can fill that need! Put the word out there. It is all connected!

Let's dig in a little further on how everything is connected. First, as we look for a suitable space to grow food, we need to know the soil's history. What has been grown there? What has been used to fertilize or control weeds? What kind of structure may have occupied the space in the past, and what was it used for? All those factors play into our decisions to grow healthy food. We are big advocates for chemical-free growing. While we were certified organic in the beginning of our farming experience, we no longer carry the certification, but we still grow without the use of any chemical fertilizers, fungicides, insecticides, or herbicides. We take no 'cides!

Let me describe our land and our farm. As I said earlier, we live on our family's 160-acre farm in central Illinois. For the most part, conventionally grown corn and soybeans surround us. We are extremely fortunate that on the west we have our forty acres of woodland. To the south we have a buffer along the creek with some woods, and the neighboring farm has about 60 acres of woods. To the north we have a road, and then across that road are conventional crops. To the east we are up against conventional cropland as well. We have planted buffer strips of fifty to eighty feet to separate us from the actual sprays used on those neighbors' crops. The woodland areas give us a great buffer. The prevailing winds are from the south and west, so that also helps in giving us a bit of safe zone around our fields. I tell you all of this to help you to understand that most properties are less than perfect. We do have great neighbors who understand what we do, and many times they will let us know a day or two ahead if they are going to have their crops sprayed with any chemical. The buffers help keep away any direct contamination, but they don't always keep everything safe from potential spray drift. Even with that, we have had very, very few issues.

A word of advice: think about your neighbors. Think about prevailing winds and any windbreaks or buffer zones you can create. Help keep any of your buffers or windbreaks in check. Mow weeds so they don't spread onto your neighbor's ground. Keep your trees on your side so they don't become a hazard for the neighbor's equipment. Work on good relations with your neighbors so they understand what it is you are doing. We are all in this together; they are trying to make a living, too, and are doing the best they can. We do not need to look for confrontation. We just need to do the best we can to take precautions to protect our crops and our food. If you have an abundance of something, take it and share it with your neighbors. More than likely they will appreciate the gesture. Remember, farming is 80 percent relationship building!

If you are looking at a potential property, consider how you can create an oasis of life. Windbreaks and wildlife habitat strips are essential in creating an environment that is conducive to life. We want as much diversity as we can possibly get. Check with your local conservation agencies to see if you qualify for any assistance in planting windbreaks or habitat strips. Even if you are not successful in getting free trees or seed, it is definitely worth planting something to give protection from wind and any chemical drift. Conifers or evergreen trees are usually fast growing and are somewhat less susceptible to chemical interference than deciduous or hardwood species. They also do a great job of slowing fierce winds.

Picking

Even annual crops benefit from the diversity we seek to instill in the rest of the farm.

Photo Credit: David Laspina

In our early years we were able to plant nearly five acres of recreated prairie. We seeded nearly 120 species of flowers and grasses into the area just east of the woodland, between it and the north vegetable field. That area is now home to a rich diversity of insects, plants, and animals. We have hundreds of dragonflies, bees of all kinds, praying mantis, and spiders! In the spring we watch and listen for the woodcocks to return and begin their springtime courtships. We have frogs, toads, snakes, and tons of other songbirds. The prairie is a medicine chest for our honey bees. Everything is connected to everything there, and all that life spills over into the cropland adjacent to it. We have beneficial insects, birds, and bats flying around all the time. All of this is really important to us. We continue to look at other ways to increase the diversity within the cropland. We can interplant some crops with seed for a future cover crop that will succeed the current crop. We can plant a crop of Dutch clover and then strip-plant our squash into it. That helps to conserve moisture, to keep weeds at a minimum, and to create a place for bees and other beneficial insects that will interact with the squash plants. Not to mention that the clover is feeding the soil microbes and helping to create an even better environment for the future. We see so much diversity on our farm.

Be mindful of the land you are looking for or planning to use. Look at the long-term possibilities for you and your property. Spend some time on the land. Dig in the soil. Listen for birds and insects. See your property throughout the seasons. Think about the crops you wish to grow. Will you need to irrigate? Will you need to harvest with equipment, and if so, how much turnaround space will you need at the end of the rows?

Rule #2:
Everything Goes Somewhere

The second rule is that everything goes somewhere. If we apply chemicals, they go somewhere. When we leave trash to blow across the landscape, it goes somewhere. Likewise, if we work with nature and are taking great care of our soil and applying proper nutrients or

Winter

Even in its dormant months, the diverse farm maintains an abundance of life.

Photo Credit: Kris Travis

biologicals, those nutrients go somewhere, too. Think! Think about the consequences of your decisions. Even when we use our nutritional foliar sprays, those go throughout the whole plant, and what isn't used above ground gets exuded out into the root zone for future use. This idea of interconnectedness is so totally amazing. It truly is a web of life.

Rule #3:

There Is No Free Lunch

The third rule is that there are no free lunches. Because everything is connected to everything, if we pull on one string, it affects something else. If we don't acknowledge our place in all of this, we can get overtaken just as easily when someone else pulls on a string. If you want something, there is a cost, one way or another. I know there are a lot of very generous folks out there, and I have met a ton of them. But I also believe that in order for that to continue to happen, I need to pay it forward or backward. Soil health is not to be taken for granted, nor is anything else. In any relationship you have to give good to get good. Again, think about the desired outcome. How are you going to get there, and what resources are needed to achieve your goal? We have to factor in something for resources.

When we talk about no free lunches, it isn't necessarily that we have to spend a lot of money or time to keep the wheel turning. Here is an example: In the first couple of years of taking product to our restaurants, we kept asking ourselves how we could show our appreciation for what the chefs were doing for us. We decided one holiday season to do some baking. We baked 120-dozen caramel rolls. When we took those to the restaurants to be shared with the kitchen staff, the results were astounding! We had one of the restaurant owners near tears when she said, "You have no idea what you have just done. In all our years of being in business, no one has EVER cooked for us; they just always expected us to cook for them."

All we were doing was showing our appreciation, and that tiny act of kindness continues to be passed back and forth to this day. It is the relationship that we are feeding!

Let's fast-forward from the caramel roll experience to 2015. That year was a near disaster for us. In a normal year we receive about forty-two inches of rain. That year, during a six-week period in June and July, we received over thirty-two inches of rain. It just wouldn't stop! We had planned to double our production that year, but we actually ended up losing over 75 percent of all our crops. There were lots of crops that we couldn't even plant, weed, or cultivate, and least of all harvest. Although nature was not kind or nice that year, there were a number of things that saved us.

First, we had a lot of diversity. While we had planned to have more crops to market, we had to sell every bit of every crop that we did have. To that end, the restaurant that was so taken with what we had done for them, told their staff that all the farms were struggling and that whatever Spence Farm had, even if it was something that they didn't normally use, to figure it out and buy it. That was huge in so many ways. We ended that year with sales still above what we did the year before. That was unbelievable. Everything is connected to everything, everything goes somewhere, there are no free lunches, AND Mother Nature always bats last! Even in our best planning, preparing and dreaming, Mother Nature has the last word.

Rule #4:
Mother Nature Bats Last

Nature will always win, as time is on its side. I read once that the sum total of our influence on the earth has not been positive. I am sure that if we took away the human influence on the planet, nature would right our wrongs.

Working with nature doesn't guarantee that disaster can't happen, but if we are working with great diversity and nurturing our soil and crops, we can often buffer the effects that nature imposes. For example, applying great nutrition on our crops won't stop a hail storm, but it will allow those crops to survive and thrive. This past spring, we were transplanting our pepper plants and had nearly one-third planted when a serious hail storm occurred. It hailed inch-sized nuggets for nearly 45 minutes. Within a week, all of those transplants that were exposed to the storm were growing and looked amazing. We had nearly 100 percent survival of those transplants.

I feel that the response in growth was a direct effect of the nutrition that we had applied. Nature is powerful, and that power can go either way. That is the fourth rule to remember. Work with respect of the power that is there.

CHAPTER 3

Soil and Plant Health Q&A

Inextricably Linked

S oil is different than dirt. Soil is alive, and we work hard to help it to be more alive all the time. We want our land to be healthy. According to author Wendell Berry, "The true measure of agriculture is not the sophistication of its equipment, the size of its income or even the statistics of its productivity, but the good health of the land."

Finding land may not be easy, but I encourage you to learn to be as resourceful as you can. Look, listen, and find the best situation that you can. Then what? Start increasing the soil to the highest level of health you can. We started by planting alfalfa. We grew the alfalfa for a neighboring cow dairy. They did the cutting and baling. We received a price-per-ton produced. Then, as we had demand for produce and livestock, we began inching our way into that alfalfa field. Just having that field in a legume with long roots made a difference in the soil conditions. We also began applying compost as often as we could. We asked the city of Fairbury if we could take their leaves that were collected each fall. The city agreed to bring them out by the truckload for free and dump them at the field's edge. We would then turn and work them into a beautiful dark compost. That compost would then be applied each fall onto the area we planned to utilize the following season.

We had soil tests done to be able to understand what shortcomings or excesses we had, and we watched our soil improve. We can only manage things that we measure. A soil test is important to understand what we are beginning with. It is a snap shot of our soil. We test our soil in the fall every couple of years, as that tends to be when the soil is at its lowest availability of nutrients. We amend as recommended with organically approved elements. In the resource guide in the back of this book is a sample soil test with optimum results. It is something to work toward.

I cannot express in strong enough language how this kind of management can absolutely propel you into a very good place in understanding the health of your plants. To understand this at the most basic level—to recognize that we can make very small adjustments in a crop's nutrients and management of those nutrients—will make a huge difference between a healthy, profitable crop and one that gets mowed off or tilled in. Learning to recognize the signs that a plant is giving us and utilizing the service of sap analysis will surely make a huge difference for you. When it comes to the 20 percent of farming—i.e. growing the crop—this information is the most important thing that I can stress.

Probably the most helpful resource that I have found to understand what is going on with our crops are the webinars put on by John Kempf from Advancing Eco Agriculture (*advancingecoag.com/webinars*). Listen and take notes. They are so informative and vital to understanding the connection between nutrition and plant health.

Toward that goal, I have asked our friend and consultant, Gary Reding, who has in the past worked with John, to give some insight to this whole process of understanding soil and crop health in a new way. We had a chance this winter to sit by the fire and talk. Listen in . . .

Fireside Chat

January 6, 2018

CROP NUTRIENTS

MARTY: So, Gary, let's get right into how we can start our crops off right and keep them as healthy as possible through-out their lifecycle. As our crops are getting started, and as they move into the framing and vegetative states, tell us what specific nutritional requirements we need to be thinking about.

GARY: Well, the emergence stage, or point of germination, is the first critical point of influence (CPI) in that plant's life, which means you need to optimize the environment for that seed to germinate. "Critical Points of Influence" is a term coined by John Kempf of Advancing Eco Agriculture; it describes the key stages of plant growth during which our management can have the most impact on quality and yield. You need to have good seed-to-soil contact, moisture, and proper depth. As far as nutrients go, the first thing that is going to come out of that seed is a root, and the primary elements you need to stimulate root growth are phosphorous and trace elements. This is why you get a good response from a kelp-type product.

M: And as we go into the coming weeks?

G: As we move into post-emergence, the seed will provide all necessary nutrients for the plant until it starts photosynthesizing through its first leaves. Once that begins, you move into the frame-building stage, which requires a good amount of calcium upfront to help determine the number of cells that will divide while the plant is starting to build its frame. Then you also need a little (but not a lot!) nitrogen and potassium to stimulate vertical growth.

M: How important is zinc at that point?

G: Now we are talking about secondary nutrients. Zinc is critical for the utilization of phosphorous in that it acts as a regulator of phosphorous. So, we like to have zinc available at the same time the plant needs phosphorous. And you're going to need zinc throughout the life of the plant, as it is a less-mobile nutrient.

M: What do you mean by "less-mobile nutrients"? What nutrients are less mobile?

G: Well, let's start by saying that calcium and boron are the two least mobile elements. Less-mobile nutrients are those that don't move around within a plant during the course of that plant's life. So, a plant requires a constant source, or an opportunity to take up the less-mobile nutrients throughout its life, because once it is in the plant tissue, it stays there. Calcium and boron must be available each day of the plant's life because those nutrients don't transfer from old leaves to new leaves. Once it is in the plant tissue it stays there—not to be shared with other parts of the plant. Most of the trace elements are actually moderately mobile. But not calcium, boron, and zinc.

M: So, if we don't have good zinc levels, we may not have good phosphorous action as that plant germinates?

G: That is a possibility, yes. People are starting to see the value of zinc, because it delivers bigger, greener leaves. That's well known by the ag industry, so they've added zinc to give the plant the visual appearance of healthy growth. But yes, you need zinc to optimize your phosphorous efficiency.

HEALING YOUR SOILS

M: We have a lot of people ask us how to begin to heal their soils when they first start out. What do they do? How do they begin as they think about planting food crops, especially if their crop land, garden, or field has been in conventional crops?

G: First thing, treat it like you are buying a new farm, even if you've owned that farm for a while. Think about buying that farm for this new purpose. Would you invest this money to purchase that land, renovate, and build it up in order to put out your new crop? There are three fundamentals to evaluate when it comes to soils: physical structure, chemical characteristics, and microbial life.

If I were to look at a piece of property to determine if it is suitable for the crop I want to grow, I'd start with the topography, of course. Is it suitable for tillage and/or working, or is it more for perennial crops? You'll need to look at the physical attributes of the surface of the soil, then at the physical structure of the soil, because if it's been compacted, misused, eroded, whatever, it will not sustain biological life in order to regenerate on its own.

You'll need to evaluate the compaction layer. Use a penetrometer to determine how deep you can go before you hit 300 psi, which is the "magical" level where roots will not penetrate. If the penetrometer has to push more than 300 psi to penetrate that soil, the root cannot penetrate that soil. So, that will be your first limiting factor. Just like the critical points of influence in a plant's life, this is a critical limitation of the soil.

Next, we look at the chemical characteristics of the soil. Keep in mind though, that if you don't have the right physical characteristics, you can't amend the soil to improve the chemical characteristics. Chemically, we are talking about nitrogen, phosphorous, and potassium (N, P and K) primarily, but I also want to know about all the trace elements and micronutrients. The next step beyond that would be microbial life.

M: And so, we're gonna look at the physical structure, understanding the compaction layer, how that soil's been treated historically. Next the chemical aspect—the nutrient makeup through a soil test. Then is there a way to evaluate biological activity?

G: There are several ways. There is new testing coming out now; for example, the Rick Haney test, which is a good biological assay of the microbial life in the soil. This new test is a little more complex and doesn't have as long a track record as, say, soil tests, but it's still a very valid way to look at things. Outside of testing, you'd look at the characteristics of your soil structure, specifically the amalgamation of soil particles to root matter. By amalgamation, I mean stickiness of root particles due to the metabolites produced by microbes and/or worms or larger arthropods in the soil. And the simplest way to gauge biological life is to just smell it! It should have a rich, earthy aroma. No smell at all may indicate that it is basically inert. If it smells like alcohol or formaldehyde, the soil is anaerobic.

M: Earthworms would be another indicator of good biological life, right?

G: They would be one indicator, although I have seen soils conventionally farmed for a long time that had good populations of earthworms but didn't have the microbial population needed in the soil yet. So it is possible to have earthworms without a healthy level of microbial activity in the soil. Earthworms are the bigger contractors; they come in first as earthmovers and are critical to good biological life, but they're not necessarily an indicator that good biological life is happening in that soil.

M: If we do soil compaction tests with a penetrometer and it's coming back at, say, 400-500 psi, what do we do to help rectify that?

G: In addition to the reading on the penetrometer, you also need to note the depth at which the compaction layer starts. You might get the probe in just four inches and suddenly it will hit 300 psi and you think that's not so bad, but then you get eight or ten inches and it jumps to 800, 900 psi, or beyond. That will tell you that you've got layers from shallow tillage. But you really need to find where the bottom of that hardpan is, and that may require some deep ripping or tillage. I know some people are diametrically opposed to that idea, but it is a matter of time and money, in combination with your goals for that operation. Mother Nature will heal all our stupidity wounds, but it takes time. So, if you don't have time because you have to pay the bank loan next year, not five years from now, then you might consider some deep tillage. But always consider the secondary impacts that tillage might cause.

M: What secondary impacts should we be concerned about?

G: Any tillage will disrupt the microbiome or the environment in which the microbes live, disrupting the mycelial growth of the fungi (assuming you have biological activity). As compaction increases, biological life decreases. If you are trying to rectify a severe compaction situation, you're not doing much damage to the biological life because it simply doesn't exist in that soil.

Other secondary impacts could result from timing a deep tillage poorly. Spring tillage can be particularly detrimental to your fields. If you get a wet spring, your water percolation will go way deeper and can cause a situation where tractors can get stuck in the deep trenches.

Also, the direction you till can change the direction of the flow of water through the soil profile. In most instances, contour direction is best for deep tillage. If you don't do it in the right direction, you can cause severe erosion as a result of your tillage.

M: Then we've done our soil test, so we have that to go on. Is there a best time to perform a soil test? Is there a best time to make nutrient applications?
G: If you are now just starting your farm plan, I would start right off with a soil test—the day you get access to your property. You can make some minor adjustments based on the time of year you've done the tests. But for the repeat testing, I recommend doing it in late summer, at the peak of growth, toward the end of a cropping season, so you can find out what your mineral depletion levels may have been. You also find out what your biological activity might have been. Additionally, it allows time to get your test results back and make amendments after your crop comes off. I like to have certain nutrients applied in the fall so they break down over the winter. Others that are more volatile or soluble should be applied in the spring so they are there and ready for spring.

M: OK, so what nutrients do we want to apply in the fall?
G: Well, if the soil tests indicate a need for calcium, you'd be looking to do an application of gypsum or lime, depending on the pH of your soil. If you have a low-pH soil, you definitely want to apply lime in the fall because it takes time for lime to break down. Lime will raise the pH of your soil. If your soil pH is already higher than optimal and you still need calcium, gypsum is your best option. In contrast, gypsum is more immediately available to the crop. On occasions, I will recommend a fall application of gypsum, but only if there is a cover crop which is still green throughout the winter that can use the calcium. Generally speaking, it is better to apply gypsum closer to spring since it is water soluble. It will provide about 90 days of calcium availability.

With lime, you generally want to plow it into the soil, so it is often a better option if you are already tilling.

M: And we're not putting mineral nutrients on frozen ground, right?
G: Right. I don't care what you're applying. Whatever you are putting on frozen ground is going to slide off if it rains before the ground

thaws. Even with manure, I've seen disastrous results when applied to frozen ground. Now if you are going to knife through that frozen crust, that's a possibility, but that's not the same thing as just spreading an application. It must be in the ground, and it must get covered. And, we never apply amendments on wet ground. If that soil is wet enough to compact, stay off of it altogether.

M: OK, so those are the less soluble nutrients. What about the more volatile ones?
G: Nitrogen is the first. Fall-applied nitrogen, or some would say any applied nitrogen, is a waste. If for some reason you are going to apply it, doing so in the fall is even more inefficient than in the spring because it's water soluble, plus it volatilizes through nitrification. You can lose up to 30 percent over the winter.

M: So, if we are looking at an organic operation, and looking at using manure as a nitrogen source . . .
G: Well, it depends on the use of the manure, what it's for, and the level of stability of that nitrogen. If it is in a stable form, and it's got a lot of humates around it, then it's probably okay. You might want to have more time for the microbes to metabolize it, though. If you put it on in the spring too close to planting time, even if that crop is a high-nitrogen-demand crop, it will give a spike of nitrogen too early and block out some of the calcium, phosphorous, and other elements that you need to build a proper plant structure.

COVER CROPS
M: OK. Next up. Cover crops.
G: Yes. Next question? Haha!

M: OK, OK. What should we plant and when?
G: Both answers are dependent on your farm, your crop, your water availability, and your temperate zone. The basic rule of thumb is if you are going to have a parcel of land without a crop for thirty or more days, put a cover crop down. Even if it only grows a couple inches, it's going to add root matter into the ground. If you look at a sprout, the roots are way deeper than the tops are, so what you are looking for is conversion of energy into that soil, with any opportunity you can. In farming, I think it was Sir Albert Howard that said we are harvesters of sunlight and water. The more days you can harvest that sunlight and

water, the better farmer you're gonna be. So, if it's thirty days or more, I'd plant something. What you plant depends on your crop rotation and the nutrient content of your soil. If you've come out of a crop that had a lot of excess nitrogen, then you want to capture that nitrogen. Put a nitrogen-accumulating crop in there that will stabilize it into plant form, and that way, microbes can release it later in life.

Now, sometimes you want a potassium accumulator, as a lot of conventional soils are high in potassium. If that was the case with your soil, you'd plant something like oats or rye—oats being a little better than rye. They accumulate that potassium, store it in their leaf material, and when it gets worked into the soil, it is waiting for the microbes to release it when called upon! But not before! It is no longer in a water-soluble form.

M: So that's potassium; what about nitrogen? What would be a good accumulator there?
G: All your grasses. On the cover crops, I like to look for something with a reducing root zone—I talked about oats—oats, rye, buckwheat, things like that have a reducing root zone, whereas wheat is oxidizing. When you have a reducing form of root zone, it increases your micronutrient availability. It helps with the microbial life a little better.

M: What do you mean by "reducing root zone"?
G: Many of the metals and trace elements, like manganese, zinc, iron, boron, etc., usually exist in the soil in an oxidized state. The oxidized versus reduced state has to do with the valence charge on the ions. To put it simply, most metals are only taken up by the plant in their reduced state. In the oxidized form, most are not available to the plant.

Some crops have more acidic root exudates that allow them to reduce those metals, meaning they can change the metals in the soil from an oxidized state to a reduced state. So, the cover crop that you choose can either advance or tie-up nutrients.

M: How about overwintered cover crops?
G: I like to first look for a cover crop that serves the purpose you need. Then determine if you want something that will winter-kill so you don't have to worry about it coming back as a volunteer next spring. A lot of root crops are pretty good cover crops—they accumulate nutrients quickly, put it in their leaves, and freeze off and die. And they don't come back next spring. Oats is another good choice; if you

use spring oats in the fall, it will not overwinter. If you plant fall oats, you'll have oats next spring! So, you need to remember the difference between spring and fall oats.

Rye is another good choice because it will grow and continue to grow all winter long, even under snow. It can be busy all winter long. But you have to know that come spring, it's going to come out with a vengeance and you have to be ready to deal with it. You'll have to kill it before you plant your next crop.

M: We see a lot of conventional farms in the area plant a fall cover crop, maybe rye or a mixture, in say October, but then about the middle of December they will spray it to kill it.
G: That's because they don't want to take the risk of it coming out in the spring. And often guys will fly cover crop seed into their corn fields, and that is to get more time on the ground to grow. Of course, we don't advocate Roundup in any way, shape, or form, on the nutritional side. But it is an effective tool for killing any sort of crop or weed.

M: If we're going to work this cover crop in—let's say we have rye that overwinters—we need to work that into the soil early, but not so early that we're doing it when it's too wet. But we need to get it done several weeks ahead of getting our crop planted.
G: A good rule of thumb to understand is that most of the crop residue of a cover crop that's worked in will probably put you into a nitrogen deficit state for about forty to forty-five days. It takes about forty to forty-five days for the microbe's biological activity to be vigorous enough to get a nitrogen release from that crop. And that means forty to forty-five days of microbial-friendly environment—not frozen ground. So, if you work it in, figure it will take forty to forty-five days until you are going to get a nitrogen release from that crop.

M: In my mind, there is a benefit to putting out a cover crop of mixed species: oats, radishes, kale, forage kale, and all those things. Each of those crops will accumulate different nutrients and release those again.
G: They also feed different microbes. Having such diverse microbial life as a result of a mixed cover crop will benefit your main crop in a couple ways. One, it gives that crop a better chance of having the right nutrition in the soil when it needs it. And two, it makes that main crop better able to handle variability, be it from irregular weather

patterns, pest pressure, or other irregularities. So, a diversified cover crop is good. I've know people who've gone as high as eight to twelve different varieties. The best thing to do is to take plant stand counts, see what survives, what thrives, and what does best for your soil.

M: What is a plant stand count?

G: A plant stand count is the number of live plants in a specific area. When you're planting a primary or cover crop, you should always know how many seeds per acre you are sowing. Now if you take into consideration the germination rate, which is the percent of seeds that will successfully germinate according to the label, you can estimate how many plants you expect to emerge. If you plant a hundred seeds with 92 percent germination rate, you can expect ninety-two seeds to emerge.

Once the crop has emerged, you can check its survivability in your environment by comparing expected plants per acre to the actual numbers of plants.

M: So, the cover crop is serving a number of purposes. Nutrient accumulation is one, weed suppression is another, but also preventing soil erosion is another huge factor.

G: You can also take into consideration when you are evaluating your cover crops what the soil temperature under those crops will be. That may be drastically different based on the crop you use. Some will shade and hold moisture longer than others. Others will die off and let more heat in. So, you have to use those factors in your decision-making process.

TO TILL OR NOT TO TILL

M: Moving on . . . there are folks who are big advocates for no till, and there are advocates for tillage. How do we know what to do when we are just starting out?

G: To till or not to till, that is the question. I like to take the practical approach rather than the philosophical approach. You've got to balance the good and the bad of tillage. Mother Nature only has a couple tillage tools: animal hooves, freezing and thawing, earthquakes. Things like that will make a physical difference in the soil profile. Mother Nature is really, really good at what she does, but she is also awful slow sometimes. If we're gonna do this within one human lifetime, we might have to help her along, but we must make sure we're helping her more than we're hurting her. I have done some soil renovation with a one-time tillage and a perennial crop following which worked wonders. Had I not done the tillage I wouldn't have gotten near the progress I did. When you're doing the tillage, make sure you're doing it in line with her needs (Mother Nature's). That may be contour tillage or minimal tillage. The rule of thumb is to do as little as possible, so you have the least amount of negative impact, but get the job done on time.

OK, SO YOU'RE READY TO PLANT

M: Alright, so we're ready to plant a crop. We've tilled, we've planted and tilled in our cover crop. What should our basic program be in the spring?

G: Start the fall before! You need to know what you're gonna do next year before you start the end of the first year. Plan accordingly, get your testing done, put down your amendments, and/or fall tillage (remember that some tillage is much better done in the fall than the spring). You could use the functions of nature to enhance that tillage you did, like the freeze and thaw cycle in the northern part of the country. People in the south won't have that option. So, to start the next crop, we look again at the physical structure, chemical characteristics, and microbial or biological life. But our priority now is biology.

Let's assume you've got your physical and chemical structure in order. Ideally, I would have stimulated the biology in the soil in the fall, and I'd re-stimulate it in the spring if possible, depending on your crop and budget.

And always make sure you pay attention to the physical structure —you don't want to plant or do any soil preparation when it's too wet. You want to make sure you're getting good seed-to-soil contact. You also want to ensure you've got good levels of the primary nutrients, depending on your soil type and your tests. If you get a good biological program going, a regenerative program, eventually you won't HAVE to put anything in there.

M: What does that mean, "stimulate the biology"? How do we do that?

G: I like to use a biological stimulant. You can get them from different companies. The ones I use are a molasses-based product with humates, which give the microbes a home. The sugars in the molasses and other natural sweeteners give energy to the microbes to start metabolizing any crop residues from previous seasons. Fish hydrolysate is a good one to use, along with any kind of calcium amendment. If you do these all at the same time, the microbes will help work on the calcium and other elements and make the nutrients more available next spring.

M: And we can repeat that in the spring?

G: I would do a seed coat treatment with microbial life. Even though you're only putting microscopic amounts on the seed coating, those microbes replicate so rapidly that in twenty minutes they've lived a whole life cycle and have three generations lined up behind them. So, I would try to do that again in the spring, in the row, on the seed. Or on the seed before you put it in the ground. You could also repeat the soil broadcast stimulation if your budget allows.

M: There are folks that believe that the native soil biology is enough, if fed properly, to be the sole source. If we are bringing in other strains of microbes to compete with what's natively there, are we hindering or helping?

G: Good question. It's a good debate. I would propose that we don't know enough about the billions of different diversifications of biology that are out there. I feel that when we put them all in the same society, they will sort themselves out and the good will prevail.

M: Are we wasting money?

G: I don't believe so. My advice is if you have a limited budget, spend your money on the biology, provided you've got the structure and basic chemistry taken care of in your soil. If those are off, you WILL be throwing your money away, because the microbes can't live in a home they can't build. I believe that the best will prevail, and that will be determined by the plants you put in there. When you're growing a crop, that crop signals its nutrient needs to the proper strains of microbes. And those proper strains will prevail in the end. I don't believe that any of the beneficials that you purchase and apply would be antagonistic to other beneficials in the soil.

M: Once the crop is up, and it's emerged from the soil, how do we know we have a healthy-looking plant?

G: Well, it depends on the crop of course, but generally, in the frame-building stage of the lifecycle, we can look at the proportions of the plant: height versus width, thickness, and sturdiness of the frame. The first true leaves that come out—the hypocotyls—are developed only from what's in the seed. But after that, the width of the leaves in proportion to the length of the leaves is a good indicator. And until you have a really healthy crop, you won't know how short and fat they can get. A long, skinny one is generally less advantageous, even in a corn crop that has long skinny leaves. You'll find, with proper nutrition, the width of a corn leaf can get two to three times wider than it normally does, and it may not get as long.

Next you look at the girth of the stalk and the amount of root mass that is being built. Most people forget to look at the roots once the plant emerges from the ground. But you gotta sacrifice a few plants. Dig them up, because half of that plant is underground. If you're only looking at the top half, you're missing half the story. Pay attention to the root structure. I don't like to see a lot of long skinny spindly roots. I like to see a lot of lateral branching going off on the side of the roots. If you look at the roots, they will tell you what's coming. Roots can only take up nutrients from the tips of the root hairs. They can't take it up through the sidewalls. If there aren't any root hairs on the sides of your roots, you're not getting optimal nutritional uptake.

M: And how can we affect that crop at that point? What do we do if we notice poor root structure?

G: It's probably an indication that you're either short on water or waterlogged. Remember, water is your number one nutrient, but it can also be your number one curse. Water availability in the soil is key to root growth. If you've got too much water, that root is going to run until it finds something with minerals in it. Or it's just going to brown off with lack of oxygen. Oxygen follows the water into the soil, but if you fill it completely with water, that oxygen is displaced.

M: Ok, so as that plant is growing, how much nutrition does it need as it's framing?

G: Interesting question again. If you think about the cycle of conventional ag, we like to put fall-applied nutrients, mainly for the convenience of getting it spread across a lot of acres. We like to do a spring-applied fertilizer program to get it ready for the crop, then we do a big in-row punch to give it all it needs to get through the emergence and growth stage. That would be akin to having a baby born at the hospital and giving it six years' worth of food before it leaves. And then saying, "Go out and grow on your own!" So, that baby may grow really fast for the first week or two, but after a while it's gonna get hungry.

M: And the nutrition might not be there by the time it needs it!

G: Exactly. Or it might have fed another crop you didn't want (called a weed). More often it will cause an imbalance in the frame building stage, meaning it will be tall and lanky. It'll be a plant that can't stand up by itself. Then the insects and disease come in because they know it isn't strong enough to survive. Then you have to deal with all of that.

M: So, a better way is to provide a good seed to start with, good biology for that seed, and once it's up we need to incrementally feed that crop.

G: Yes! If it's possible. The other way to do it, which is the way Mother Nature does it, is to provide a slow and steady constant supply through the microbial release of nutrients tied up by the organic matter in the soil.

M: What should we look for as a "good" organic matter figure?

G: In the soil test? A lot of soils are down to about 0.9%, which is basically humus. We've farmed everything out of it up to that point. And as bad as you can farm, you can't farm the humus out of the soil. For most of the corn belt soils, especially out here in Illinois and west of the Mississippi, you're going to have higher organic matter from what the prairie grasses created. But not nearly as high as they did have at one point. As you go further east, that organic matter may fall off rapidly due to rainfall and a lot of other factors. As you go farther west, organic matter falls off because of oxidation. So, a good soil can have 3–4 percent organic matter. A better soil can have up to 10–15 percent. Some pre-mixed man-made soils can have up to 35–40 percent, but they become their own challenge to achieve balance.

M: So, on our farm, when we have our crop up and going, we typically apply weekly foliar feeds. Is there a better time of day to apply foliar feeds than another?

G: Ok, get ready, we're gonna get fancy! The best time of day is when you optimize your "point of deliquescence." That is the time during which the optimal temperature and humidity around the leaf itself, and within the canopy, are reached, such that the nutrients can be metabolized, or taken up, by the plant through its own methods or by the microbes on the surface of the leaf. There are many millions of microbes on the surface of the plant that work just like the microbes in the soil. You want that environment to be optimized at the time of the application, which means you'll want to apply your foliars somewhere between 3 and 5 a.m. If you have too many acres to get it done in that amount of time, the next optimal time is in the evening. So generally, two hours before sunset and up to two hours after sunrise are probably your best window of opportunity. If you do apply a foliar and it does dry off in the middle of the day, it won't be taken up or activated until you reach that optimal point of deliquescence in the next cycle. But in the meantime, you may lose some.

M: Back to frame building. What kind of minerals should we be looking at as we're framing?

G: In the frame-building stage, we want to build strong bones, like we would in our children, our animals, whatever. Of course, bones are made of calcium and phosphorous, and roots take phosphorous to be stimulated to grow. We need calcium to allow cell division to occur in the plant's growth process. So, we would back off the nitrogen and potassium early in life. Remember the discussion about the children and how much you would feed them—little bits more often? A small plant has a very minimal nitrogen and potassium demand, so there's no need to preload your nitrogen and potassium like they do in conventional farming. It will only compete against the calcium. So, we need primarily calcium and phosphorus and the closely associated trace elements, which would be boron and silica for calcium, and zinc and iron for phosphorus. Then as the frame grows, in a couple weeks, before it goes into reproductive phase, you want to start pulling the switch and bringing in a little more potassium.

M: Do we also need manganese there?

G: Ah, the king pin! Manganese is one of the elements that has been depleted and neglected in the system. Manganese helps regulate potassium. As you get further west, you get into much higher potassium-type soils. A lot of farms have high potassium from over-application. If you're trying to get calcium into a plant, potassium competes against it. If you can get your manganese up to a certain level, it will help regulate the potassium uptake to only what the plant needs, and allow the calcium in. Manganese also has a major influence on reproduction. It's the strongest reproductive micronutrient and it also helps protect against a lot of diseases and insects, primarily by allowing the calcium in to build a strong cell wall. So, we talk about zinc regulating phosphorous and manganese regulating potassium, but I would like to look at it also that it helps stimulate calcium by regulating potassium. And it is the key to getting calcium in. Three things you need to regulate or assist calcium uptake: boron, silica and manganese.

M: As we are applying foliars, can we apply too much? How much are we wanting to run off the leaves? Do we just want a fine mist? Does the "more on" principle apply?

One more quick note: the quality of your water for foliar sprays is extremely important. Instead of using our well water, we now use only rainwater to mix all of our nutrition. The pH is much better, as is the electrical conductivity. Again, we can only manage what we can measure. Check your water! For too long we were applying these foliars using our well water and didn't check the pH or EC and were not getting the full benefit of the nutrition we were applying. Once we switched to the rain water, the effectiveness of the sprays was much improved!
— *Marty Travis*

G: The "more on" principle does apply, but in the sense that you DON'T want to be putting more on! With foliar applications, the whole idea is to give a little bit more frequently. Also, your crop value, labor cost, etc., need to be considered. A good rule of thumb to think about with foliars is that most of the time a little dab will do ya. We use foliars for trace element optimization because so many of the micro and trace elements get tied up or chelated in the soils or are unavailable just by being distant from the plant. When you do a foliar it's right there and very quick. Foliars provide a quick uptake, whereas soil applications provide a voluminous uptake, but slower. Too much of a foliar can smoke a crop pretty quick.

M: Are those foliars hazardous to the applicator?
G: Well if you're considering using an agrina phosphate fungicide, yeah! But if you are talking about a nutritional foliar, I haven't run into any nutritional foliars that are harmful to humans. Or insects. Or bumblebees. Even a conventional salt foliar won't be harmful at the trace levels applied.

M: Okay, so we're putting on our foliars, typically once a week, early morning or evening. How do we know that it's working?
G: Do your plants look better? That's the first thing. Some foliars create a faster response than others. There are some radioactive tracers that they've done on cobalt, and it only takes 8 seconds to get from the leaf to the root tip where it belongs. Pretty remarkably fast.

Potassium acts pretty quickly because it is highly mobile. The plant takes it up quickly. Nitrogen acts quickly. Some calcium applications take more time to show. So, it depends on what impact the element has on the plant as to how quickly you'll see a response. But most often you'll see a response in 24 to 48 hours, and if not, at least by the next weekly application. If you don't see the response you would expect from that element being applied, then try increasing your concentration.

M: How should we increase it? By applying a higher concentration or by more frequent feedings?

G: If you do not think you are getting enough on, you can either apply another application sooner than one week after the first or you can put it on in a higher concentration of the solution. You can adjust to what you feel the plant is needing by either timing or rate of application.

M: You mentioned to adjust by what we "feel" the plant needs. How do we get beyond the concept of what we feel that plant wants? How can we measure what it needs?

G: I always like to measure! You can manage the measurement of your foliar applications by thinking in units applied per acre applied, or per 1,000 square feet for gardeners, and adjust accordingly. That feeling interaction you get while looking at a plant is enhanced if you can give it a digital association through sap analysis. That's probably where my awareness of looking at a plant and seeing where the deficiency or toxicity in the plant came from. It is from working with sap analysis and getting the data to correlate to what I was looking at in the plant.

M: Can you tell us how the sap analysis works?

G: That's a secret! Hahaha! The sap analysis technology is a way of testing the plant's "blood," or sap. It is like taking a sample of our own blood to test for a calcium deficiency as opposed to taking a sample of bone to test. If you have a calcium deficiency show up on your bone density test, how long was your blood deficient in calcium before it showed up on the bone density test? It could have been weeks or months or even years. Well, if you have a plant that has a life cycle of 120 days, you do not have weeks and months to determine the deficiency or toxicity. The sap test uses a technology to extract the liquid from between the plant cells without rupturing the cell walls. It is using only the free-flowing sap in the plant and not using any of the larger quantity of elements that are already built into the structure of the plant tissue. By measuring element levels in the sap, we can get an indication of an elemental imbalance two to four weeks sooner than if we did a tissue test. We can get the results back just as quickly as a tissue test, but by getting this two to four-week jump on a diagnosis, we have more time to implement a remedy. And the plant has that much more time to overcome the imbalance.

M: So, we have the crop up and growing, and we have been making our applications . . . and we come out one morning to find all the squash plants are covered with bugs. And some of them are dead. What happened?

G: I don't know what you did wrong!!

M: Uh huh.

G: You got out of balance somehow.

M: Somehow?

G: The problem is your plants are covered in bugs. What kind of bugs? Little small sucking insects?

M: Probably early on it will be cucumber beetles, corn root-worm beetles; later in the season it will be squash bugs.

G: The insects you have indicate different imbalances. The small sucking insects generally indicate you have too much nitrogen, and the plant is not able to metabolize that N into amino acids and proteins.

M: Could that be because we do not have enough biology in the soil?

G: That could be the case, or it could be too much N applied. If you have good biology in the soil producing good N for the plants, it won't be like you are putting too much nitrogen on. Plants don't respond the same to applied N as they do to biologically "generated" N. The biology will produce more complex nitrogen forms like amino nitrogen. The small sucking insects do not have the enzymes to digest those amino nitrogen forms and therefore do not come to eat on the balanced plants.

M: So, small sucking insects like flea beetles on the turnips, radishes, spinach, or arugula and other greens crops would be a result of . . . ?

G: Those could be a result of high nitrates, or it may not be too much applied nitrogen but a deficiency in molybdenum, magnesium, or sulfur. Because it takes those three elements to convert the nitrogen into an amino form in the plant through photosynthesis, a deficiency in any of them will cause high nitrate or ammonium forms of nitrogen in your plant sap, making it appealing to the small sucking insects.

M: What we have found to alleviate all manners of the flea beetle problem was a small application of molybdenum and it totally, totally took the problem away.

G: Sure! And what you did was supply the key ingredient that was missing. Molybdenum, or "molly," is the central element of the nitrogen reductase enzyme, which is required to reduce the nitrate nitrogen so that it can be synthesized into an amino acid chain. If you don't have molly, you don't have that enzyme, and you won't build complex amino acids and proteins. It is water-soluble and a trace element. You only need a little bit, but it is essential. Without it, you cannot complete the photosynthetic cycle, throwing the plant off balance. If the small sucking insects get the signal that the plant is out of balance, then they do their job, which is to get less-than-healthy plants out of the environment. They do this by eating them and converting those plant materials into their own bodies and excrement in order to recycle the nutrients in the sick plants back into the soil. That means that the remaining healthy plants can then utilize those nutrients to produce nutritionally-balanced fruit.

If you have larger insects with more complex digestive systems taking complete bites out of leaves or stems, then it is a case of not having enough calcium and/or silica in your cell wall structures. This goes back to those early applications of calcium in the frame-building stage of growth. It could also be that you have not reached the level of plant health and energy where your plants are able to produce complex lipids and fats. After that an even more advanced level of plant health exists, in which your plants can produce secondary metabolites or essential oils. These are the elements it takes to gain complete resistance to insect damage.

LEVELS OF PLANT HEALTH

M: Let's talk more about these progressive levels of plant health.

G: Okay, the four levels of plant health and resistance progress like this: In the lowest level, the plant starts producing more complex carbohydrates. Once it gets to the complex carbohydrate level, you will gain a resistance to many of the root diseases, like phytophthora, fusarium, verticillium and others. If your plants are suffering from some of these issues, you know they are not achieving the first level of plant health. If you have not achieved this level, then the subsequent levels are increasingly difficult to reach, and you will have many other issues in your crop.

The next level of plant health is where your plants start to metabolize complex proteins. Your plants will eliminate the small sucking insects by producing the longer-chain amino acids and complex proteins, making it resistant to those small sucking insects we talked about earlier.

The third level is where the plant has enough energy that it will start producing lipids, or fats, and even more complex carbohydrates. With this level, you can have plants that are resistant to powdery mildew, downy mildew, and all sorts of airborne fungal and bacterial diseases that plague so many crops. You can tell when you reach this level by the wider leaves in proportion to the normal length you might see. They will be thicker and shinier. This is due to the lipids the plant is building to store the excess energy for later use in fruit development.

The highest level of plant health is when the plant has enough energy to produce very complex oils and other compounds that are the real resistance tools. These are the essential oils we consider so valuable and have used as medicines and remedies for many ailments. This is the level where your plants will be resistant to the larger, more complex digestive systems of the munching insects. It is the plant's secondary metabolites that are the strongest protection mechanism of the plants against the big insects.

M: And it takes good nutrition and good biology to achieve that.
G: Balanced nutrition and balanced biology. Correct.

A lot of our root diseases are caused by microbial life that are normally beneficial to the plants by providing nutrients to the plant in return for food. If the microbes get any signal that their host plant is not healthy enough to feed them, then those same beneficial microbes may start to consume the plant that can no longer feed it properly; or they will die and leave room for other antagonistic ones to consume it. They are trying to recycle any sick plants into the environment for use by the remaining healthy plants.

M: And a sap analysis will help determine what nutritional imbalances we might have.
G: The sap analysis technology is very good. If we're helping a new farmer get familiar with the concepts of plant nutrition, I'd use sap analysis as a tool to do that. It is the best way I know how. I'd ask the farmer to pick out an average part of his or her field that represents the majority of their crop performance and have them do at least three tests the first year. One early in the season during the frame building stage, one

during the reproductive stage and then one during the fruit fill stage. If the crop is a longer-season crop and has higher value, I would recommend that they take samples every other week throughout the season. If it was a shorter-season crop, I would do sampling as often as weekly.

M: This is because the plants' nutritional demands change through the season, and we can measure those shifts.
G: Yes. Plants' nutritional demands change very often, from every week to sometimes even daily, or even hourly, depending on the crop and the stage of growth. So the more we know about that the better we can manage it.

Often, I will work with a new farmer who is frustrated with their crop and where it may be headed in the middle to end of a season. I will suggest that we do a sap analysis immediately, even if we cannot improve this crop this year. At least we will have an idea of what imbalances are happening at this time of the season. If we get as much information as possible on this poor crop, we can better plan a program to fix those problems in the next year's production.

I was able to take sap analysis two times on an Arizona potato farm one season just before the plants were to go into senescence, which is when they start maturing and dying off. We designed a fall application of nutrients and then built the spring pre-plant and planting applications, as well as other foliar and side dress applications, which made for a very successful crop the next season.

M: Many times we think we are near the end of the season and we just think, "Let's get it over with," but there may still be something to learn.
G: Absolutely. Any day the plant is up and living, there is something we can learn about it.

REPRODUCTION AND FRUIT FILL
M: Alright, so, we have our tomatoes, peppers, squash, or whatever, and they are up and growing. They are starting to blossom and set fruit. What is happening nutritionally in that plant now?
G: That is a shift, similar to what happens in our teenage years when we go into adulthood. There is a shift in hormones as well a shift in nutritional demands. During the frame-building stage, the plant is running on a slightly higher level of auxins than cytokinins. These hormones are both always present in a plant during development;

however, the balance between them shifts. Auxin is a plant growth hormone that is produced in the rapidly growing shoots and tips of plants, and it promotes vegetative growth. When the plant gets to the end of the frame-building stage, where it is no longer producing new growth tips or shoots, the auxin production slows, allowing the cytokinins to dominate. Cytokinins are the reproductive hormones that stimulate flowering and pollination. So, to illustrate the nutritional balance shift that occurs, remember we wanted the calcium and phosphorous in the plants early on. Calcium is truly a growth mineral and phosphorous is truly a reproductive mineral. But you need both to get the right vegetative growth and proper fruit development. Let's look at calcium: It has been shown that 80 percent of the calcium in a cherry when it is picked was in the bud of that cherry ten days after mid-bloom. If the calcium is not in the plant sap by then, it will not get in that fruit and it will suffer some (or many!) fruit quality issues.

I usually recommend a cytokinin and calcium application two weeks before flower on an annual crop, and again one week before flowering. This will keep the plant balanced more toward the cytokinin production for flowering and pollination. Once you get to where the fruit is starting to size, say maybe 20 percent of its final size, you need to shift back to the growth side of things to fill that fruit. You will need to increase the potassium and nitrogen to produce the weight. The potassium assists in moving the sugars to the fruit and expanding the cells that were determined by the amount of calcium present at blossom time. Potassium builds larger fruit.

M: And there again our manganese is going to help regulate that potassium.

G: Yes. And remember I said that manganese is our number one reproductive trace element? As a matter of fact, most of the micronutrients are reproductive dominant. Manganese is just the most reproductively responsive. Boron will help with pollination and fruit retention on the stems or in the pods. Copper gives the flexibility of the skin coat, which is probably more of a vegetative action. Most of the others assist with the multiplication or retention of the progeny of the plant.

M: So, as we evaluate our fruit crops, how do we know if we have sufficient nutrition?

G: That takes a little bit of studying. As far as the mobile nutrients go, the plants will tell us—they do not lie. And again, sap analysis will give us that information. We will sample new leaves separately from the old leaves and have the analysis run on them for comparison.

When I say a mobile nutrient, that means those that the plant can move around based on where the plant needs it. Remember: the plant's number one goal in life is procreation. Its primary goal is to produce one high-quality offspring. If it has enough quantity and balance of nutrition, it will produce more seeds or progeny, as allowed by the nutritional balance and supply. Plants go for quality first, quantity second. Plants put the optimal balance of nutrients nearest the seed first. So, we look at the new leaves, knowing that the optimal balance should be there, and then we look at the older leaves, knowing that any excess will be stored there for possible later use. If the plant is short on one of these mobile nutrients, then it will pull it out of the older leaves to get the optimal balance closer to the seed by sending it to the newer leaves. Those primary mobile nutrients are nitrogen, phosphorous, potassium, and magnesium. Sodium and chloride are also very mobile essential elements, but plants do not need very much of these. If you have too much sodium or chloride in your soil, it will show up in your plants by the old leaves having much higher levels in them than in the young leaves. Any time that the old leaves have more than 15–20 percent higher ppm of a mobile nutrient than your new leaves, you know you have a toxicity. If you have 15–20 percent less in the old leaves than the new leaves, you know you have a deficiency. We can use this information to quantify how much we need to apply in the next foliar or side-dress application. The sap analysis is good enough that if you see a deficiency or toxicity of greater than 20 percent in your test results, you will see a phenotypic exhibit of that issue on the plant.

If we can balance those primary elements, it helps to make it easier to balance the remainder of the elements. We also look at different ratios between elements. We look at the potassium-to-calcium ratio, the phosphorous-to-magnesium ratio, and many others.

M: We are looking at a tomato or a potato or a pepper. How do we know if we have a good one?
G: By looking at the fruit without measuring it? Do you mean without the use of sap analysis?

M: Yes.
G: Well it helps to have a few years of experience reading the sap tests throughout the growing seasons to help dial in these concepts and correlations. Fruit quality issues like shape, scarring, size, skin coat issues, hollow tomatoes or potatoes—most of these issues fall on the back of calcium deficiency.

Firmness is another good indicator of fruit quality. Potassium provides firmness to fruit, provided you have enough calcium to make a good cell wall. Without enough calcium, the potassium could expand the fruit to the point of breaking the skin open or cracking it. Fragile skin or bark could be due to calcium deficiency. I've seen cherries crack during the ripening period if there is a rain, and this is caused by calcium silica and copper deficiencies. Copper helps with the flexibility of fruit skins.

M: How about the yellowing at the top of a tomato? Streaking yellow starting at the top.
G: Now that is most often caused by a potassium deficiency during the ripening of the fruit. Potassium moves sugars (and salts) around in the plant sap. If you do not have enough, there is an incomplete ripening of the fruit that shows up as a yellow streaking radially out from the stem.

M: If we have splits in the skin, then that would be caused by a calcium deficiency?
G: Yes, generally that would be the case.

CROP RESIDUE

M: What should we do with our crop residue before the next crop or winter?
G: Well that depends on the crop and the time of the year that your season ends. It also depends on what you have planned for the rest of the year and what your next crop will be. Remember the goal we set at the beginning, to keep the ground covered with something—so residue is good. There are a lot of pathogens that survive and thrive in crop residues. I prefer that the residue be biodegraded by good biology in and on the soil surface. Sometimes that means you will want to incorporate that residue to get it into contact with the soil and the microbes living in the soil. Sometimes you may just want to leave it on top to provide shade and/or erosion control.

M: Let's say we have a tomato crop and we determine it had blight. Do we need to remove that crop residue to protect the next year's crop? It could be the same with squash and other crop diseases.

G: Generally speaking, no. It depends on how prevalent it was throughout the field. I would suggest you work it down and inoculate it to biodegrade it. That is, not oxidizing the residue but metabolizing it. If you get enough of the beneficial microbial life metabolizing the residue, it will prevail over the pathogens. Then you need to address the real reason you had the blight or powdery mildew in the crop. If you look at the sap analysis it will help show you why, and then you can address the balance of nutrition. If you get your nutritional balance in place, you can inoculate plants with these pathogens and the plants will not get the disease. Destroying the residue alone will not guarantee you will not have the problem in the next crop if you don't get the nutrient balance right.

M: It's a lot like people who get multiple kinds of cancer.
G: Yes, or like doctors who see sick people all day but do not get sick themselves.

M: Okay, so I have an orchard. Does all this apply to that as well?
G: If it's green and photosynthesizes, yes.

M: Conventional crops, corn, soybeans, and all the others?
G: Yes, if it's green and photosynthesizes, yes.

M: What about livestock in their pastures? Is there anything we can do to make their forage the best it can be?
G: Yes. Everything you do in your orchards and vegetable fields applies to forages too. To be honest with you, it's probably where your next best vegetable field will come from: optimally balanced nutrition on pastures that have been eaten by livestock and redeposited onto the soil. When this happens, you have every natural cycle involved to regenerate the soil. You have every complexity of nature built in.

M: On a side note, OUR beef is amazing.
G: It gets better with good forage too. And you've got good genetics.

M: We raise Dexter, which is a small breed. We have another farmer that is doing Angus. Our Dexter was 806 hanging weight. Their Angus had hanging weights of 703 and 636.
G: Do you know why?

M: Part of it was age and part of it was genetics.

G: They weren't over twenty-four months, were they?

M: The Dexter was. And he got bigger. All of them had a crazy amount of marbling and fat, more so than all the others that were coming from our other farmers. We had a mixed legume pasture with about 40–60 percent legumes. We are having steak tomorrow night.

So, is all this more expensive, more work? How do I know if it's worth it?

G: Yes, it can be expensive, depending on where your starting point is. You need to determine the value of your crop as well. There can be a program built for anything in the whole range. It can be achieved.

I myself achieved nutritionally balanced crop production with the highest yields and highest quality without applying any of the foliars, but I did apply livestock as a tool. The whole concept is to emulate nature as close as possible. Now, throw in the little caveat of cash flow and you have to do it as quickly as possible. Those nutrient applications, tillage and all the crop practices are part of your accelerator or breaking system of getting you where you want to go. I had addressed my soil structure and chemically balanced its nutrition before putting it into a perennial pasture through small grains and companion cropping. It stayed in pasture for two years while intensively grazing it. In that two years I doubled my organic matter and Cation Exchange Capacity (CEC) and did not have to apply anything thereafter. But I used those livestock in a rotation from that point on, and I used the manure, which I did not have to haul very much because it was more of what I call the "direct deposit manure application technique" instead of storage and handling. When you can get to the truly regenerative stage of soil management, just like a forest in nature, it doesn't need anything added to it. It is going to be difficult for us because we are always taking something out of the equation by harvesting and selling something, but it is possible. My costs were significantly less than when I was conventionally farming, and my margins were much better. Now if you do not have the management skills or resources to do livestock management, or if your crops are just not suitable for livestock in the rotation, you will have to make up for it in some way. Anything you cut out of the natural cycles of Mother Nature will have to be supplemented somehow, some way. If you pull livestock out, you are going to have to do something to emulate the hoof traffic in chipping the soil surface to allow moisture to penetrate. Or you may have to replace the microbes that come from the mouth or the backside of a cow. What you take away determines what you will need to replace.

M: Are there instances where we will need to look at other crisis management tools?

G: Help the neighbors?

M: We have been doing that as much as we can. So, we have done all these things with foliars and soil management and we still have a disease or a bug issue. It really comes back to the fact that we can only manage what we measure, and we are not measuring very well.

G: Or you are not interpreting what you measure very well. There is a thing called the Rule of Five Whys. If you ask the question why something happened and do not get the answer, ask why again and again until you do get to the root cause. If you ask why five times, you will usually find the root cause. We think we are pretty smart with all our sap testing, soil testing, and soil biological assay testing, but I will tell you what: Mother Nature has more variables than the best computer in the world with all the best algorithms could possibly compile and analyze. We don't know what we don't know, except that there is a lot more that we need to learn. If we assert an influence that Mother Nature does not like, she will tell you about it. It may show up as an insect infestation, disease, or yield loss. Or she may be nice to you and give you a nice yield result with high quality, but that's because we were doing nice things for her. If you have a crisis, the best thing is to go back and look at your data on everything you did to the crop and the weather patterns. Nutrition will not protect you from experiencing a hail storm. However, I have seen instances where nutrition helped minimize the impact of a natural disaster like hail. I saw it in a field of chili peppers in Arizona. The farmer was able to pick one portion of the field where he was trialing a complete nutritional program against the usual program. After a bad hail storm, he was able to harvest 70 percent of his crop from the better nutrition side, where he could not harvest any of the conventionally fed part.

M: This spring we were transplanting our peppers into the field and we had an afternoon hail storm. We never lost any of the peppers.

G: They had good growth tips on them after the hail then. If the growth tip is good, it can usually grow out of the part where the damage occurred.

M: It sent us to the porch. It was bad. Does the foliar program replace soil amendments?

G: I would have to say that you can build your soil amendment program up to the point where all you need is foliars, or that you could get to a point where you don't even need the foliars. Mother Nature does not do foliars except what comes out of the air.

M: But if we give extra foliar nutrition, it eventually goes to the soil.

G: That is correct. You are opening another topic of debate. Conventional wisdom says that if you build a healthy soil, you will get a healthy plant. The methodology of conventional ag that I was trained in said we needed to replace whatever we took out of the soil plus 10–20 percent for soil building, or leaching, depending on how you look at it! If we get a nutritional balance of the soils at an optimal level rather than a built level, then the need for the foliar applications is diminished. I look at the foliar applications as a quick but small-scale adjustment to nutrition. Soil amendments are the long-term, larger-scale and slower adjustments part of the program. If you feed a plant to its optimal health by tweaking its foliar applications, then that plant's improved energy will be converted to root exudates (secretions from the plant back into the soil) that will build your soil. So, if you have your basic soil chemistry relatively balanced, you can fine-tune the plant through foliars and then the plant will be the final balancer of the soil. It will put exactly what it wants back into the soil and you will have a healthier soil for the next crop you plant the next season.

M: How do these root exudates improve our soils?

G: When a plant metabolizes its nutrients through photosynthesis from the harvesting of sunlight and water, it will convert that energy into new plant, fruit, and root growth. If all the demands of the plant are met, i.e. the frame building, root growth, pollination, fruit setting, and fruit filling, then any excess energy goes out through the root into the soil as sugars and proteins to feed the microbes in the soil. The microbes take up those sugars and proteins into their own bodies and can then metabolize any carbon in the soil from previous crop residues or whatever, until their lifecycles are over. All of that is stored in the soil as a plant-available fertilizer. So, it really is the storage battery of the soil system. You can tell what that storage capacity is by knowing the Cation Exchange Capacity of your soil.

M: Yes, you mentioned CEC previously. What exactly is that?

G: The Cation Exchange Capacity is comparable to the size of a fuel tank in your soil. It tells you how many units of nutrition your soil can hold, and it is directly correlated to the amount of organic matter, as well as other physical properties of soil. Organic matter is the source of carbon which the microbes metabolize into their own bodies. When those microbes die, they become a plant-available carbon source for plants. You can actually store simple compounds in the soil through the exudates feeding the microbes.

You know when you pull the roots out of the soil, and particles of soil stick to the roots? That sticky stuff is part root exudates and part microbial metabolites that are causing soil particles to stick to the root.

M: Can you talk a little bit about the bacteria and fungi in our soils? What are they and how are they important?

G: Bacteria metabolize small ionic nutrients and/or compounds into slightly more complex compounds within their own bodies.

Bacteria take in, break down, and formulate both simple and complex sugars and proteins. They handle many trace element interactions between the plants and soil. Bacteria are immobile; they do not move unless they get flooded or the soil gets eroded. The bacteria signal to the fungi what the plant needs but they are basically stuck in one spot. The fungi, on the other hand, are a more complex life form that have mycelium that can branch out to around 600 feet into the soil. The fungi metabolize the bacteria when they die and turn the bacteria bodies into more complex compounds that the plant can take up. This conserves the amount of energy that a plant must use to make a compound from single elements. The fungi produce pre-fabricated compounds for the plant. This is how the food chain continues well below the surface of the soil where the plants reside. It goes down into the microbial population and then back up into all the soil insects, arthropods, and other creatures I don't even know the names of but love dearly. Then you get to the worms, which the birds eat to further feed the plants with their droppings. So, you have a complete food chain below the surface of the soil that many folks in agriculture do not even concern themselves with.

Microbes are a huge population of diverse workers we need to respect more, even though we cannot even see them. There are millions of them and many kinds of them that work tirelessly on our behalf if we just give them half a chance. They work hard every day without any complaints, the don't take any time off, they make their own shelter, and they all have green cards.

You might have seen electron microscope photos of fungi attaching to the side of a root. That is the closest the root will get to taking anything up through its walls. The connection between the root and the fungi and the fungi and the bacteria are the network that communicates the needs of the plant. If the plant needs manganese from the bacteria and there is none in its local area, the bacteria signals to the fungi who then looks all along the 600-foot-long mycelium for manganese until it finds some. The fungi metabolize it and then can shunt that compound through its mycelium back to the location where the original signal came.

M: So, a really healthy soil will have loads of bacteria, fungi, and other microbes in it.

G: Absolutely. And insects. But it is all about achieving balance. Most pesticides are broad-spectrum and kill the good with the bad. They also can cause chelating issues that interrupt the mineral interactions. Often if you spray a fungicide, you will get an insect problem within a couple weeks. I've seen cherry growers spray a fungicide for powdery mildew and then within two weeks they have a problem with spotted wing drosophila. That is caused by the fungi no longer being able to transport all the necessary nutrients to the plant.

SUMMARY:

So, wow, are you a bit overwhelmed with all of that information? There is a lot to digest there. But know that this is the basis for your success. We have to begin with a great understanding and a foundation of healthy soil and plants. Go back and read again and make notes. Understand the concepts that relate to the beginning, middle, and end of the season. Think about this soil and plant health universe as an ongoing learning opportunity. Compare what we have learned here with how it relates to our own body and its health. The soil is the digestive system of our farm and is quite similar to our own digestive system. I know how valuable this information will be to you. It has made a huge difference in our experience at Spence Farm.

CHAPTER 4

A Photographic Field Guide

S ometimes a picture is worth a lot more than a wordy description. But we also need to know and understand what we are looking at. The following is a sampling of actual plants and soil conditions that may help you understand what to look for and then how to help make things better.

The first order of soil health revolves around soil structure. We must address that first before addressing the health of our crops. Take a look.

Cloddy Soil

There are several reasons why it may be difficult to work soil down into a fine seedbed or transplant bed. High-magnesium soils with low calcium availability are some of the most difficult to work with, especially when they are low in organic matter, as shown above. Cloddy soil also can be caused by working any soil type that is too wet on your primary (first or heavy) tillage pass. Never work the soil too wet and you can avoid many of these situations.

Sandy Soils

Even very sandy soils like this California field can get compacted if worked too wet. Sometimes in our rush to get the next rotational crop growing, we get back out on the soil before it dries to the proper level. Some crops, like celery, may need watering all the way up to the day of harvest, which then makes it difficult to harvest the crop without trafficking across wet soils. These are decisions that need to be evaluated and managed to minimize negative impact.

Soil Breakdown

This central Indiana soil was farmed in seed corn production that requires significantly high equipment traffic over the years. There were multiple applications of many herbicides and insecticides that also contributed to the breakdown of the soil structure. As this photo shows, the spelt seedlings just emerging in the still-visible seed slots are struggling. Some of the weeds are doing much better. They are trying to repair the damage caused by poor management.

Soil Compaction

The same field as in the previous photo. When pulling up the shovelful of soil, you can see all of the horizontal fracturing that is indicative of the multiple layers of compaction. This limits air and water infiltration into the root zone, restricting growth. The penetrometer readings on this soil were well above the 300 psi range at a very shallow depth. Anything that is more than 300 psi indicates some compaction. Also, pay attention to how deep the level of compaction is.

Treated Soil Compaction

Again, the same field as the previous two photos. This portion of the field was treated with a biological stimulant and a complex microbial population to help mitigate the soil issues. The farmer wanted to maintain a no-till approach, so the progress will be slower than using tillage to break up the layers of compaction. The microbes, however, are getting to work making the soil surface crumblier and therefore more permeable to water and air.

Irrigated Field

This irrigated field of organic corn in western Kansas is on a rotation of wheat/fallow/corn. The common practice in the area is to run a sweep plow four inches deep during the fallow years and before planting. As you can see, there is a very hard pan (over 900 psi on the penetrometer reading) at four-inches deep. This corn plant will have to survive by only being able to go four inches into the soil. Water can only go that deep as well, so there will be minimal holding capacity before runoff. I was in this area after a two-inch rain and saw rivers of water covering county roads for miles after running off. With only fifteen inches of rainfall per year, this is a huge loss, causing the need for more irrigation.

Cherry Tree Stump

This Oregon conventional cherry tree stump was taken from a poor-producing orchard that was getting replanted. Upon using a penetrometer to see if the field had any compaction in it before replanting the new orchard, I found several levels of compaction where the old trees had grown and where the tractors had travelled between the rows of trees. I explained to the farmer that roots cannot penetrate compacted soil layers. He brought me over to his stump pile and this is what we saw. There was a compaction layer about eight inches below the soil surface that prevented these roots from growing down radially from the trunk. They went down eight inches and turned horizontal, thereby reducing the amount of soil access to pull up other nutrients locked beneath the compaction layer. No wonder the orchard was a poor producer.

Soil Penetrometer

A penetrometer used to measure the compaction of soil profiles.

Cannabis Root System

This complex and massive root system of a biologically farmed Northern California cannabis plant is indicative of a very healthy soil. This is from an annual crop that is transplanted into the soil in late May and harvested in October. A lot of carbon was sequestered into the soil profile during the growth of this plant.

Cannabis Plant

The plant that produced those roots in one season.

This organic aronia berry field in Oregon has clover sown into the
alleyways to increase the biological diversity and to conserve water. *Aronia Berry Field*
Many people think that a growing crop depletes water in soil. But in
fact, the increased organic matter it provides improves water-holding
capacity and improves the microbiological populations that then
store nutrients gathered from the air. The different microbes that have
symbiotic relationships with different crops can serve the main crop
as their roots comingle under the soil surface. This practice provides
more energy harvesting of the sunlight and water that falls between
the rows and provides better soil structure, allowing water and air to
permeate the soil. It also helps prevent compaction when the equipment traffic becomes a necessity to manage the main crop. Mother
Nature never allows her soil to be bare.

*Many people think that a growing crop
depletes water in soil. But in fact,
the increased organic matter it provides
improves water-holding capacity.*

Organic Spinach

This is organic spinach displaying a severe calcium deficiency. There was too much potassium and nitrogen applied before planting, causing rapid growth but weak cellular structure. You can see the bubbling appearance with collapsed cells between the bubbles. This is due to poor cell wall strength from a lack of calcium during the cell division stage of growth. When the cells expanded from the potassium uptake, the walls ruptured, causing them to collapse. This increases the susceptibility to downy and powdery mildew—a huge problem for the spinach industry.

Peach Orchard Bark

The cracking of the bark on this organic peach orchard in Oregon is a clear sign of at least a calcium uptake issue. This could be caused by a boron deficiency as well as not enough available calcium. It may also be because of too much potassium. There are many nutrient interactions that can cause deficiencies, and sometimes it is not because you have too little of the deficient nutrient but because of too much of a competing element like potassium.

Peach Orchard

The same peach orchard as in the previous photo. Note the severe peach leaf curl. This again is an indication of poor calcium uptake. You can see cellular collapse as well, we saw just like in the spinach leaves.

Blackberry Crop

A very healthy Oregon blackberry crop in the making. Note the size of the leaves. This is due to proper calcium uptake early in the season, providing larger surface area on the leaves for more sunlight capturing. This improves the photosynthetic energy needed for a very large crop.

Tomato Plants

These tomatoes are in the fruit fill stage of growth. You can see that there are some fruit quality issues resulting from an imbalance of calcium and potassium earlier in the growth of these plants. By having too little calcium uptake relative to potassium early in the season, blossom end rot occurs. The yellowing and burnt older leaves are because the plant, which is now in heavy fruit production, does not have enough nitrogen or potassium to handle the fruit load. You want to provide for early calcium uptake and then, once the fruit is 20 percent of its finished size, increase the potassium and nitrogen to fill the fruit.

Blueberry Plants

The purple older leaves in the two photos above of young blueber-ries indicate low phosphorous uptake. You can also see some purple on the stems of the plants. Applying an available phosphorous would help these plants recover fairly quickly.

Purple older leaves and some purple on the stems indicate low phosphorous uptake.

Cannabis Plants

Nitrogen and phosphorous are two of the mobile macronutrients. This cannabis plant is suffering a combination of nitrogen and phosphorous deficiencies. The older fan leaf yellowing indicates the nitrogen and the slight purpling indicates the phosphorous.

Blueberry Plants

This is a classic image of a manganese deficiency combined with a sulfur deficiency in blueberries. It took this Oregon organic farmer two years to remedy the situation through applications of elemental sulfur, manganese, and gypsum.

Squash Plants

Here is a photo of a potassium deficiency in squash. You can see that the symptoms occur in the older leaves more than the new leaves, indicating a mobile nutrient issue. Nitrogen, phosphorous, potassium, and magnesium are the macronutrients that are most mobile, as well as sodium and chloride. The edge burning with yellowing of the older leaves progressing into the middle of the leaves indicate potassium is deficient.

Orange Trees

This is a conventional orange grove in California showing symptoms of manganese deficiency. Note the interveinal chlorosis (yellowing) of the new leaves. The cause of this is the multiple applications of glyphosate under the tree line to maintain weed control. Glyphosate chelates manganese, zinc, and other micro-nutrients, leading to a condition called citrus greening. This is a major problem in the citrus industry these days that needs to be remedied before it destroys the industry.

Wheat

Pesticide damage to a wheat head after a poorly timed 2,4-D application.

Flowers

Nutrition can also play a role in achieving more flowers per stem, larger flowers, and brighter-colored flowers. These Wisconsin flowers were fed with some of the high-cytokinin kelp (to get shorter internodes and more buds per node), high-energy fish hydrolysate with crab shell and shrimp shell (to help in energy supply to make larger flowers), and some manganese, cobalt, phosphorous, and copper. Copper aids in enhancing color of flowers and fruit.

Tomatoes

Good nutrient balance can lead to a very successful crop. This Wisconsin greenhouse tomato farmer was having the best season ever after getting all of his nutrients in balance.

Vegetables

These vegetables were picked two weeks before this photo was taken. There is no degradation of quality, despite being kept on the counter at room temperature in northern California. The farmer later sent me a photo of the same bowl of vegetables that looked the same. Improving fruit quality increases storability, thereby increasing your marketing window of opportunity and shelf life at the purchaser's home or restaurant.

Cherry Crop

This Oregon cherry crop is an example of "Roping Cherries", which can be accomplished by getting enough calcium into the plant prior to the cell division stage. In perennial crops, this point is shortly after harvest, when the plant is determining its balance between the vegetative and reproductive phases right after harvest the previous year. Fifty percent of the calcium that will be in the fruit is there before mid-blossom and 80 percent by ten to fourteen days after mid-blossom. Because cherries blossom before putting on their leaves in the spring, you must get the calcium in between harvest and blossoming. Manganese, phosphorous, and other reproductive nutrients like cytokinins also play a major role in accomplishing good fruit set.

Cherry Crop Leaves

The same Oregon cherry crop as in the previous photo. This farmer made the statement, "Bigger leaves equals bigger energy equals bigger cherries equals bigger money." By increasing the surface area of the leaves, you increase the capture of sunlight, which increases the photosynthetic energy in the plants. These are the biggest leaves ever seen in this variety of cherries in this region.

A Chef's Field Notes
On Farm Learning!

A Chef's Field Notes on Learning the Farm

I suppose ignorance was the best way to describe how I felt on my two-hour trek back to Chicago after spending an afternoon at Spence Farm. I had so many questions that I never knew I wanted the answers to. I had been cooking for over ten years at this point and was a few months from opening the doors to my first restaurant. I knew what I wanted for the restaurant: a simple approach to super-seasonal, honest food, cooked and served by a team that was dedicated to those ideals. What I didn't know was that lunch that afternoon would change the scope of how I cooked and ran my business for the remainder of my career.

Marty, Kris, and Will welcomed me into a place that was foreign to me. My experience was suburban and urban, not crossing lanes into rural or farm territory. As I toured the farm for the first time I was impressed with my hosts. They were listening. The tour was not a one-sided diatribe into the world that is Spence Farm. We would walk and talk, slowly getting to know one another, explaining our general purposes and goals for the near future. I was put at ease by their genuine hospitality and curiosity as to my purpose for the visit. We spoke of seasonality and how their farm was treated as a living, breathing organism that had to be taken care of, nurtured, and exercised. There was a genuine excitement in speaking of produce both mundane and obscure and a truth in reasoning for why they had chosen the path of raising heritage–breed animals, They looked to history to guide their decisions to link themselves with foods nearing extinction. All subjects that could be spoken of with bravado and self worth; and yet, as I was introduced to my first paw paw tree, there was nothing but humility and reverence for what had been provided on this land for this family to work with and steward for the future.

I began to see Marty each Wednesday on his weekly sojourn to Chicago to deliver his food to many of the city's restaurants. He would stop in the back door and drop off the five pounds of this and five pounds of that along with some random odds and ends that he thought we might enjoy. The discovery process through these visits was vital to the energy of our small kitchen. As my cooks and I would ruminate, Marty would watch, sometimes quietly comment, and often give a lesson on origin, flavor profile, or ripeness based on the time of year. And then he would listen. His presence was calming even in the busiest of times, and as soon as we saw the green van pull up we would drop what we were doing in order to spend a few moments to take a deep breath and converse with Marty about everything from produce, weather, what was new in the restaurant, and often our own families. It became almost a ritual, one that I still look forward to nine years later.

I have had the pleasure of spending a fair amount of time on Spence Farm. Selfishly, I look at it as a sort of graduate school for both myself and many midwestern chefs who have had the pleasure of being educated during a visit or two. We have harvested vegetables in the rain and tasted eggs directly from the chickens running around the farm. We have been educated on ancient grains and soil health and have dispatched a number of animals, all of which I can remember as clear as day as I write this. We have met amazing human beings who are dedicated to the practice of proper agriculture, both for their livelihood and for their health. We have been welcomed on the farm as students, teachers, advocates, cooks, bakers, fundraisers, butchers, field hands, and often as family. It is a relationship that has matured over time. As all things will change, the relationship has grown to see things further than the field, the restaurant, the local grocer.

As time has progressed, Spence Farm has grown, with the goal of teaching a new generation about the importance of our food system. This is at the center of their ethos, and any boundaries or hazards that may lie in the way of the progress of that education are met with both humility and an intense scrutiny. It is with patience and purpose that their business model has grown, using Spence Farm as the focal point for a nexus of farms to find success in selling their food to restaurants, grocery stores, CSA programs, and many other creative outlets. This has allowed many small family farms to maintain and sustain their way of life in the agricultural community. It is a model to be proud of, a model that could have a positive effect anywhere around the globe. It is a model that needs to be shared.

These days I don't feel quite as ignorant as I did nine years ago. I have witnessed change within agricultural communities fueled by Marty's vision for what can be. His positivity and insight are a force to be reckoned with. I believe in his methods and his message and look forward to being able to peel back his thought process one page at a time.

Chris Pandel, chef at Swift and Sons, Dutch and Docs, Chicago

Tomatoes

CHAPTER 5

Where Does It All Go??

Chefs, Groceries, CSAs, Farmers' Markets

I think one of the hardest things for some farmers is how to sell the crops they grow. How do we make those connections? What do we need to do ahead of time to know that we can monetize our production? Which comes first: the crop or the market? Conventional crop farmers just take their corn, beans, or wheat to the elevator in the nearby town and off it goes. They may not always get the price they need, but their crops always go somewhere. The same with their livestock. Many farmers take their hogs, sheep, or cattle to the local sale and take their chances on getting a decent price for them. We have taken a different approach.

From the beginning, we wanted to have our produce and meat sold to consumers who would enjoy and appreciate the work that went into producing it. When we began, we knew we didn't have the capacity to produce large amounts of anything. However, we did experiment with a small farm stand and took some items to the local grocery store. But we realized early on that we had an amazing opportunity to work with the chef community. In doing so, we could develop relationships with those chefs and grow items that they were most interested in serving to guests in their restaurants. We knew how much they could use per week or per season. Then we took their weekly orders and harvested and delivered that amount. We received payment for that product and came back to the farm with an empty van and no wasted produce.

So how do we begin to understand how to sell? There are many things we have learned through the years. First, I think a healthy understanding of the market is super important. Before you start planting, do some research. I'm not just talking about market research; also learn what your soil or land can produce. What you—yes, you—can produce. Not all farms can grow great melons or great potatoes. What are your dream crops? What will it take to produce enough to sell? How much is too much? You will want to research what options you have for marketing those crops. Are you producing something that is just the same as the farmer down the road?

A couple years ago, Will and I were at a growers' conference and were having lunch at a table with a few other farmers. One couple began telling us about their new venture. Neither of them came from a farming background but had bought a property and had planted several thousand apple trees! When we asked what varieties they had planted and how they determined those varieties, they replied that they had gone around to all the neighboring farmers who produced apples and decided to plant the same as those folks. When we asked how they intended to market all of these apples, they weren't sure; maybe just a roadside stand. When I asked if they had anything that would set them apart from their neighbors or if they had other back-ups for any extra production, they hadn't thought about that either.

Similarly, we had another farmer call one year asking if we knew where they could sell their three acres of currants. The currants were ready for harvest and they had not made any contacts for folks to purchase them. I tell you all of this because I want you to succeed. We have to have some sense of where it all goes! I realize sometimes it is hard to know what "all" is. I realize it is hard to sell a crop that is still growing or hasn't been harvested yet. Sometimes it takes a sample for someone to get excited about buying it.

But, please, please, understand that the market is extremely important to your success.

Remember, start small and work your way up. Get comfortable with growing your crops—growing outstanding, quality crops! And get comfortable talking to people.

When you talk to folks, remember that your passion may or may not resonate with them. Just because you are growing this amazing row of rainbow-colored Swiss chard, not everyone eats it, nor will they want to hear a fifteen-minute sales pitch! But here are a few things that may help.

Listen. Listen to what folks are talking about on their menu or what they are feeding their families. Another way to learn what chefs may be interested in is looking online at specific restaurant menus. Look at the ingredients they are using in their dishes. Look to see if they list other farms on their website or on their menus. Look at enough restaurants to get a general idea of what is being used seasonally. I am not saying that a specific restaurant is going to buy your product, especially if they are already getting it from another farm. What I am saying is that all of this will give you an idea of the types of crops that are being used. It is also important to understand whether that particular restaurant even uses local product.

One of the resources we used early on was *Chicago* magazine. It has a listing of many of the best restaurants in the city. We scoured those listings looking for any that made mention of using local farms or seasonal menus. We also tried to focus on any that were more than a single star or were a bit pricier. Then we did some online looking to see what their menus were like and came away with a better understanding of the world that those chefs work in. Many other cities throughout the country have similar magazines or listings.

Sometimes there are opportunities for interaction at events designed to connect with either chefs or CSA members. We have seen not-for-profits or other organizations host meet-the-farmer or meet-the-buyer events. These can be great door openers. If you have that opportunity and can showcase some samples, do so. Many times your product will speak volumes about your farm and sometimes more so than you. If you can even get one person hooked, that is where to begin. Then, with continued relationship development, you can sometimes ask if they know anyone else that would be interested in what you have to offer. I believe many times it is better for someone else to recommend you than for you to try to press your case. To me, it means more to hear someone else is happy with a product than to hear a sales pitch from the one trying to sell it. Don't get me wrong—it is important for you to believe and represent yourself and your farm well; just continue to get as many advocates as you can along the way. They become your unpaid sales force!

We never really sold at farmers' markets, but I do believe farmers' markets are a fairly easy way to enter into the arena of local food. You can connect with local shoppers and develop many of the same relationships that we are talking about. Depending on the market, some can be expensive to get a booth while others may be nearly free. In recent years, we hear more and more of the experienced farmers say they are beginning to see their sales drop at their farmers' markets. This is a bit concerning and sometimes confusing. Consumers are in general looking for more local choices and looking to connect a face to their food for their families. Farmers' markets allow that kind of interaction. Some communities do offer late-season special holiday markets. This helps, as many of us still have a lot of product after the regular markets end. I think it is important to have as much cash flow coming in for as much of the year as you can.

Some of the downsides to markets are the uncertainties, such as weather, consumer schedules, consumer spending, and other farmer competition. We know one farmer who said it was their intention to have the cheapest sweet corn at the market. That really helps no one. We are all trying to make a living at this, and racing to the bottom does not help. It doesn't help the consumer understand the true meaning of producing something great. It demeans other farmers, and it also demeans that particular farmer's reputation. So think carefully about how you price your product. Think carefully about how people will perceive you and your farm. You are worth a fair price.

During the last several years, we have sold literally tons of products to our chef community. In that same time, we have had numerous folks ask us where they can buy our produce for their own use. We began with a volume/scale we could handle, which was selling to restaurants; as we have continued to expand our production, we have been able to offer more and more to the general public. One way that I have thought about this is that we as farmers should be selling our food through the places where people buy their food, regularly and conveniently. Grocery stores are that place for the vast majority of the population.

As we began thinking about that opportunity and how we could access the grocery store market, we initiated a conversation with our local grocery store family. We have a family-owned grocery store that is really quite nice, large, and accommodating. We spoke with the owners and came to an agreement that they would be happy to provide a certain amount of cooler/shelf space for local product. Instead of the store buying the product, we offered to set up the space with our product, to manage it every day or two to make sure it was still looking good, and to see if it needed restocking. In return, the store would give the farmers 80 percent of the sale price and hold back 20 percent for the space. They had little investment into the shelf area and we could work to keep it filled with items that we thought or knew would sell.

It was a good starting point. The store could use it as a promotion that they were carrying local produce and we could use it as promotion that we had our product in a local grocery store. We received a fair price for our work and were able to set the price for our own produce. The percentage the store kept was built into our retail price.

Moving forward a couple of years, the grocery store saw the benefit of working with the farming community and began purchasing the product outright. They had made it through the risky startup phase and had some sense of what was available during each season and also what folks were willing to purchase from local sources. We continued to do some meet-the-farmer events at the store; these are always a good way to connect with your customers. We were supplying local food to a place where people buy food! We now had begun to close that loop of food miles and accessibility.

Next, we had another larger family grocery store contact us to discuss a project. The new concept was to have a large store that made the connection with the farmers an important, integral, and visible part of their business. This project did not go as well. We came to understand that if we don't have everyone on the same page, working to develop the relationship extremely well, there is a real chance that not everyone is going to buy in. It looks and sounds good, but when it comes to the point of numbers, the margins often mean more than the relationship and the product.

I think there is still a lot of work to be done with grocers. Everyone needs to make it work, I get that. But, we need to have conversations about the whole experience. If a store wants to showcase verbiage and signage promoting local farms and their products, we all need to make sure that everyone realizes what that means. How is our product different than what is purchased from the warehouse or from a farmer's auction house? How is one farm's product different from another's? What about different prices paid to the farms? I will explore and share some other ideas coming up, but just know for now that we all have a lot of work to do in order to make local food more mainstream.

As we begin to think about how to make connections, consider who you know and who they know. References and referrals are super important. If you are faced with someone who says they are not interested, don't let the opportunity pass. Ask them if they know of someone else who might be interested in what you have to offer. Never take a "no" without asking another question. Sometimes it is good to start by saying, "I'm not here to sell you anything. I just need your opinion or advice. What do you think of this product, and do you know anyone that might be interested?" That takes the pressure off of the person in front of you. It also makes them feel important as you are asking for their advice. Sometimes it works out that they are definitely interested; plus, you might get another referral, or more.

Another successful tactic we employ is at the end of the year we ask several of the seed companies we deal with if we can purchase or acquire a box of their seed catalogs to hand out to our chefs. Many of the highly visual catalogs are super exciting to look through. Chefs are visual characters, and looking at a seed catalog does a couple of things. First, it allows them a window into the farmer's world. They get to see what we have access to, and this can create a lot of excitement for them. Second, they can begin to visualize specific varieties from the catalog being on their plates. This also gives them an opportunity to have something totally unique on the menu. Additionally, it helps you, the farmer, know what to grow. If you ask how much they would use per week during the season, it will give you an idea of how much to produce. This is a great way to understand how much and what items you should grow. Then if you have an abundance and can offer it to other folks or, again, ask who else would be interested in it, you have a supply and demand issue that could be nearly well matched. We always like to have the demand for any product just barely ahead of the supply, and it is okay if we run out. Better that than to have so much extra that it goes to waste. We just try to be close.

But what happens if you do have so much extra? Sometimes you can offer a deal. Take samples for tasting. Sometimes you can offer it to an area food pantry or food bank. While we don't do a lot of social media stuff, that seems to be a quick and easy way to get your product's availability out there. Be creative. Then, in the worst-case scenario, turn it into compost and keep it on your farm. There is a lot of value and nutrition in that crop, and reintroducing it into your soil is better than trashing it all. Even feeding it to livestock is a good option if it is a healthy choice for the animal.

Remember the story from earlier where we had one of the wettest seasons ever? We typically receive around forty-two inches of rain per year in Illinois. In June alone, we had over thirty inches. We either couldn't get crops planted as it was too wet, or the crops we did have were really struggling. We could hardly get onto the soil without doing major damage through compaction, and just walking left huge, deep divots. We were in trouble. As best as we could we put on our happy face, as people don't want to see or hear you complain. However, our chef community could see and understand right through that. Most of the Midwest farming community was dealing with similar conditions, all of it not good. So, along about August one of our chefs told his staff that he wanted them to make sure and support all the farms, buying whatever product they had available, even if that meant they had to use things that they didn't request or normally wouldn't use. Our chef community saved us! They stepped up and purchased nearly everything that we and our community of farmers had. That is the beauty of the relationship. They helped us through a really rough season and we won't forget that.

Where it all goes is ultimately a delicate balance of making connections. Do your best to have a good idea of who wants it before you plant or begin a season's growth. Do your best to keep in touch with your prospective buyer, letting them know about how far out the harvest is. Providing pictures could be helpful and as the crop nears harvest, and providing a first taste is always good. Don't be a nuisance, but be there. Make sure you have tasted your product so if someone asks you what it tastes like, you can honestly respond!

Remember, everything goes somewhere. Do your level best to make it go somewhere with purpose!

CHAPTER 6

Cooperative Marketing

Play Well with Others: Competition vs. Cooperation

I want to introduce another concept and a reality. Not to burst your bubble or take the wind from your sail, but more than likely, you can't do it all! Few of us can. Within just a few weeks of our beginning to grow and deliver product to our chef community, we realized we were in pretty deep. We knew we couldn't produce all the things they were looking for or wanted. They were asking for proteins, grains, vegetables, fruits, and so much more. We also saw an incredible opportunity for our community and the young people in it. We felt that we were in a unique position to enable so many more folks to realize their dreams. And so we began thinking about how we could work together with more farmers. How could we create markets and opportunities for so many more? And in doing that, we also realized we weren't really taking anything away from our farm; we were creating a system of working together for the good of all.

This all began in 2005. We saw, as many of you see, the young people in our rural communities moving away and not returning. Parents and grandparents telling the next generation that there just isn't enough here for you, too. We heard this over and over in our community. We began brainstorming and talking with our chefs, trying to figure out ways that we could create opportunities for those young people to stay on the farm and have an income if they wanted. Now, more than a decade later, we still see the need for more farmers, more opportunities, and more families working together and staying in the community. We helped to establish two cooperative marketing groups, Stewards of the Land and Legacy of the Land. Both are limited liability corporations with equal members. In the last couple of years, we have also created a separate marketing and delivery company called Down at the Farms, LLC.

The Down at the Farms, LLC grew out of the need for a separate marketing and delivery service that could serve the needs of a wider group of farmers in our area. This LLC includes farms that are members of the Stewards and Legacy and also those who are not members of the other two working groups. We have had a number of farmers come to us and say that their farmers' markets were not as profitable as they had hoped, or that their Community Supported Agriculture groups (CSA) were not being sold as well. Some were beginning farmers and had no idea how to sell their products. At the same time, the demand for more products in our chef community was growing. We needed more expert growers. Upon doubling our represented farmers, we saw nearly 100 percent growth in our sales the next year. That demand has continued. Let me share a little deeper what is going on here.

First, I'll reiterate a couple previous statements. For one, remember that what I am sharing is my truth and my personal experience. This is what has worked for us. Second, remember we only choose to work with nice people. We also have worked really hard to create equal opportunities for everyone. It is important to understand that it takes someone who sees the greater good that can come out of a community working together. This is not about who does the best or the most or needs their product sold first or offered to a specific venue. This is about a group of farmers who in most other circumstances would be competing with each other. We have turned that into a group of farmers who are now cooperating with, talking to, and supporting each other.

If we go back to the outcomes, methods, and resources model, we saw the need for more product and more farmers participating in the local food arena. Our desired outcome was to create a model that helped to manage efficiencies and communications for farmers and that also made ordering and receiving those products easier for our chefs. The method, or the "how", was to create a system of communication between the chefs and the marketing person, and then between the marketing person and the farmers. Yes, it is a middle person, but the chefs didn't want or need to communicate with over sixty farmers each week, and the bookkeepers didn't want to write over sixty checks each week to each individual farm. The chefs also didn't wish to receive over sixty deliveries each week from all those individual farms. On the flip side, most of the farmers had no desire to go driving around the city or the countryside, spending a whole day or two being away from their farm. Many of the farmers are not comfortable "selling" to chefs or others.

We began by asking our chefs, "What are you still looking for?" We then had a list of products that we had need of. We could then seek out those particular farmers who were able and willing to produce those items. That is the resource piece—the "who can do that" section.

So, to you the farmer, you the chef, or you the interested food systems person, this, in my mind, is a very viable model that can be replicated across the country and indeed the world. It requires working together, understanding the needs of the community being served, and doing it! It also requires a leader who has a clear understanding of building connections and has the time, talent, and mindset to do so.

The Nuts & Bolts of the Partnership

Let me continue to give you more insight into how this works. Here is a basic rundown of an average week, which in our case starts on Fridays.

On Fridays, our farmers upload a list of products that they expect to have available for the coming week onto a Google sheet that is shared among the farmers. Everyone lists their farm name, product they wish to offer, and an approximate amount. Then, I consolidate that list into a Word document that I send as an attachment to a Friday evening email to hundreds of chefs, grocers, and individuals.

Those recipients have until Monday at noon to respond via email with their orders—first come, first served.

As the orders come in over the weekend and into Monday, I can assign the orders to each of the farmers with amounts and to which restaurant. That way the farmers can see what is ordered early and can plan for their harvest and packing.

I confirm the orders with all the farmers on Monday right after lunch. The farmers then harvest, wash, pack, and bring all of their product, labeled with their farm name and which restaurant it goes to, to our walk-in coolers at the farm. All product is placed in labeled restaurant crates. The farmers are also required to email a final invoice to us so we can make sure that they are not short on any product. If they see that they are going to be short, they can return to that Google sheet and see if there is someone else that has the same product who can fulfill their shortcomings.

On Tuesday evening, we create the restaurant invoices and email them to the chefs and bookkeepers.

On Wednesday, we exchange goods for payment.

On Thursday, we return to pay all the farmers and to do it all again on Friday!

The Human Technology Model

There are a couple of things I wish to elaborate on with this model. We understand that there are many other technology platforms out there. We like this model because it allows for the element of human interaction. For example, there might be three farmers offering similar products. I know each of those farmers. There may be an instance in which I know that a certain farmer REALLY really needs to sell some product to pay a farm loan or to move enough product. This also allows the human perspective on being fair, assigning equal amounts as

Marketing
Our marketing meetings happen in person to allow us to take the human element into consideration.

best as we can. There are also instances when a specific chef has really liked a specific farm's carrots (or something like that). I can make that assignment and keep everyone happy based on the ordering history. I also can help those farmers coordinate between themselves to fulfill larger orders together.

Many of the farms also work together to consolidate all their orders so one farm can bring multiple farms' orders to our coolers. Many of them will take turns making those runs so they don't have so many folks leaving their farms. We are actually looking at the possibility of providing a pick-up service from farms each week if they can coordinate getting everything aggregated to centrally located farms. Our group encompasses about a seventy-five-mile radius from our farm.

In addition to the human aspect of our ordering system, our chefs have said they really enjoy and look forward to having a conversation each week when they order product. Questions are easily addressed, and substitutes are easy to work in if necessary. Additionally, we do the deliveries. Having the farmer be the face is one of the most important elements of our success. We can pre-sell so much product each week just by having a conversation on delivery days. Understanding what is working for the chef or for the farmer is paramount to making the relationship work. This is a relationship! We have to work at it, and I believe in-person is the best way to do that!

Annual Reporting

At the end of the season, our record keeping system allows us to provide a report to each farm with all the product they sold for the year, including a breakdown of each crop and to which restaurant it was delivered. Similarly, we can provide a report to each chef with all the product they purchased throughout the season. We can do a seasonality chart for each of the chefs so they can better plan menus the next year. It also gives us a means to talk about what else we can do as a group. What other products, how much, and whether or not we need to adjust anything. Again, the communication aspect is crucial.

Another great thing about our working together is the strength in numbers. We can provide a larger amount of continual product and we can provide a vast diversity of product. It is almost like a one-stop shop. Also, when we negotiate with larger grocery stores or other accounts, we have more sway than a single farm.

Problem Solving

So, where do I see potential issues for stress?

Everyone must be willing to play well together. We can't have individual farmers going straight to clients and trying to offer a better deal just to sell more of their product. While this has happened only twice in the last twelve years, both times it was our chefs who called the farmers out on it and reported them to us. Our chefs realize that there is an incredible amount of trust and goodwill involved here and they won't tolerate any end runs. We also have had a couple farmers who believed their product should have been sold before anyone else's. That creates distrust among the group and leads to competition instead of cooperation. It is the role of the middle person to facilitate order and

Celebrate
A meal to celebrate the bounty of our cooperative efforts.

cooperation. Watching out for everyone's best interest is important, and it's not an easy job. Being fair and helping everyone understand that we are stronger when we are working together is extremely important. The middle person is the key to the success of the group. I believe that we are the advocate for the farmers to the chefs and also the advocate for the chefs to the farmers. We have to understand both worlds well in order for everyone to win. I also believe that we, as farmers, have the ability to make better chefs and that chefs have the ability to make us better farmers. We must be truly invested in each other's success so that no one fails.

What does that type of investment in each other's success really mean? One specific instance happened recently. We had a number of chefs ask if we could do specific cuts of beef. We began asking each of them what pieces they were most interested in obtaining. Soon we had most of a whole animal spoken for each week. We then went back to our farmers and identified those that would be able to work together in a rotation to supply whole animals each week. One particular restaurant was taking a lot of the high-dollar primals and cutting their own steaks from that primal. They had been hand-cutting steaks for several months, so we decided that we, as the marketers, would purchase them a new band saw to use in breaking down their primals.

That act of providing them with the tool they really needed did a couple of things. It told the chefs how committed we were to them— that we were investing in their future and ours too! It ensured that they would probably continue to buy beef from our farmers, keeping the farmers busy and happy. It also just felt like the right thing to do. We have been the recipient of that kind of generosity as well. So why not return the favor? Pay it forward!

In the end, playing well with others isn't that hard. Obviously, we shouldn't give our core away, but we also shouldn't think of ourselves as so important that all else comes in second. People can see that: customers, fellow farmers, community members. Creating a vibrant farming community takes hard work, discipline, and fairness. We have the opportunity to restructure our food community. Everyone eats. Let's work to make sure all who wish to be are well fed are not hungry.

A Grateful Inheritance

— Will Travis

I've had the privilege of working with my dad every day for almost the past ten years. He's one of my best friends, and I wouldn't want it any other way. Working with family can be extremely challenging: you have to realize that everyone has an opinion, and there are times when you may disagree. But you are still family. There are days when it's best to just do your own thing.

Most days it's a lot of fun. We have a very open dialog. If you don't keep talking and dreaming about the future, you aren't going to be able to change if something happens. I know ten years ago we wouldn't have ever guessed we would be as big as we are today. It seemed that for years we doubled in size every year until we took over the entire 160 acres. Now that we are using all the acreage, we have begun expanding our marketing and delivery operations. This has been a way to help reduce the hours crawling around on our hands and knees while still spending time working together. It has also made it so that I can spend more time with my wife and daughter.

This is something that everyone needs to keep in mind when getting into farming always make time for family outside of work. I love what I do and I want my kids to want to do it as well, so making it not seem like a "job" is a good way to teach them how great it is. I hope they decide someday that they want to stay and keep the farm going just like their ancestors before them. It's a great feeling knowing that I am doing my part in the history of our family farm, and I plan to leave it better than it was when we started—to have it set up perfectly for my kids to jump into and to do what they enjoy with it.

When I look at young people today wanting to get into farming, it makes me think of all the opportunities that we have been given on this farm, and I am very grateful for them. I know that most folks have to start from scratch unless they are inheriting the operation. We were lucky to have the land available to us—we just had to be resourceful in finding equipment.

There's a lot that can be said for making friends with all the old retired farmers in the community. I've learned over the years that there are a lot of retired guys in the community that have the old equipment that still works perfectly fine; it's just small compared to the new stuff. Never be afraid to get an old rusted thing for free. Most of the time a little oil, heat, and a hammer can make it usable again. Always be open to sitting down and listening to the folks who have used the equipment, even if it was during their child-hood; they may remember just the thing that you are looking for.

There's also the school of hard knocks. Never be afraid to fail. It's going to happen, so just have an open mind and learn from your mistakes. This is sometimes the best way to learn something new. Over the years we have had too many experiences to count where something didn't work like we planned. It's just part of life on the farm. That goes with anything—equipment, weather, cus-tomers, plants, and animals.

When it comes to animals, it's easy to get really attached. You spend so much time with them and they have their own personal-ities. There is one great piece of advice that a friend told me after we had our first still-born calf and I was pretty down about it. He told me that "if you're going to have livestock, you're going to have dead stock." That has helped me over the years when it came to animal losses. It's going back to the school of hard knocks. It's also a lesson I will be teaching all of my kids as they grow up.

We work with some individuals here locally who buy product directly from us. They are a small group of women that who want to feed their young families the best products they can get. They have searched us out so they can know exactly where their food is grown. They bring their kids with them every time they get their groceries from us. It's very important to them to teach their kids where real food comes from. They want them to meet the farm-er and ask us questions. I want everybody to realize that it's not impossible to get good, healthy food from a local farm. There are people all over the world doing exactly what we are doing. Just start asking questions. Once you find a farm, don't be afraid to ask them anything. If they aren't willing to let you come see everything they do, then you need to keep looking. Make sure the farmer you work with is willing to let you bring your family out and see where your food is grown. It's so important for all of us to know where and how everything we eat is raised. That way we can make an informed decision on what we eat. I think that's a big reason why so many young people with no farming background are getting into it today.

Whether you are going to be farming yourself or buying from a farmer, make sure that you always enjoy the experience with your family. It's something very special that not enough people get to do.

"Sustainability is ultimately an ethical issue. There is no economic reason to do anything for someone of some future generation other than it is the right thing to do. We owe a debt to those of the past who created the opportunities that we have today, and we can only repay that debt to people of the future."

— Dr. John Ikerd, from the documentary Sustainable.

CHAPTER 7

Working with Family

Who's Following Behind?

I n 2030, when my granddaughter turns thirteen, our family farm will be 200 years old. Caroline is the ninth generation to live on this farm. That seems to me to be quite an accomplishment. This farm has gone through many evolutions over the years. When Valentine Darnall came to Illinois in 1830, he had to figure out a way to make a sustainable living for his family, just like each subsequent generation. Throughout the history of this farm, I am sure that has always been a difficult task. There is one thing that I have noticed, though. All of the grandmothers have come from somewhere else. By that I mean that they have all married into this family and brought with them their own identities and passions. When the husbands passed away, many times it was the grandmothers who had to keep it together and make hard decisions in order to do what was best for the farm and for the family. It has been no different in my generation or in my son, Will's.

Will and his family now live on the farm in the "big house." With that comes a lot of responsibility and commitment, including taking care of buildings and upkeep of the yard and land, as it is important to be the caretaker for this generation. When Will was ten years old, we asked him one evening what he wanted to do with his life. Seemed like a good thing to ask a ten-year-old! He said he wanted to work in the wood shop with me, make maple syrup, and take care of this farm. Well, we didn't get to spend a lot of time working at furniture building, at least not as much as I had hoped. But he has nailed the other two!

Working with family can be one of the most rewarding aspects of the family farm experience. But for some it is one of the most frustrating. I have had numerous folks say that they wish their parents would just allow them a tiny fraction of land in order to work on their dream. And a few of those folks are in their mid-40s! What is the wait about?

From the beginning here at our farm, Kris, Will, and I envisioned together what we wanted the farm to evolve to in our time. Like I said earlier, Kris was the real driver with the passion, foresight, and legal mechanics. We each played an important role in working to achieve the desired outcomes. Will is mechanically-minded, loves history, and loves working with the animals, especially the cows. I tend to be the one always looking for the latest and greatest crop or opportunity. I try to stay ahead of the pack that way, working to make connections and marketing the farm in specific ways. Kris continues to be the accounts manager and keeps us solvent. While she and I are no longer married, we still work well together as a team, benefitting each other and also the larger farmers' group.

It takes a team to do this. It takes support and a belief that you can do it together. Having family involved is something I think is hugely rewarding. There is a sense that working together is far less about accomplishments, although those are important, than about the quality of time spent and the uplifting of each person. Each of us has our own ideas of how to go about something, but sometimes it takes all our eyes and ears on a project to understand that there could be multiple paths to an end. Listening to each other's ideas is vital. I think creating an environment that allows each partner to be heard and respected is key to making everyone happy. Sometimes that can be difficult, I realize, but in the end, aren't we about working together?

As time has gone on, we three have found our own unique positions within the farm. With Will and I being "on the farm," we have divvied up our roles. We still make a lot of joint decisions, but I continue to encourage him to make more of his own choices. He is more than capable, and I believe in him. If he is going to be the person living there taking on more responsibility for animal chores, and if he doesn't want to move around the pastured hogs, then so be it. If he is more akin to doing cow chores, great! There is no sense of having to stay with the same thing forever. I certainly don't want to burn him out or make him and his family feel like they "have" to do such and such. It is their turn to accept the responsibility and to do so with the passion that they feel. That doesn't mean that I take the back seat on every ride, but I don't have to be the driver. That allows the next generation the opportunity to express their views and to potentially fail better too!

From the time Will was in high school, Kris and I made him a third partner in the farm. We took all the farm's income and split it four ways. One-fourth each to Kris, Marty, and Will and one-fourth stayed for the farm. That helped to cover any of the farm's expenses. We each shared in the abundance or lack thereof! We also didn't make it such that Will was just getting an allowance. He was a partner. He had a voice. As we have increased in our scope as a farm and as a marketing and delivery service, he has continued to expand his knowledge and participation in all aspects. He can make calls, order equipment, or talk with prospective farmers. We have a respect and a trust with each other that allows that to happen daily. We continue to pass the torch but are not dumping it all on him either.

I think working with younger children offers similar opportunities by allowing them to pick and choose things that interest them— by giving them a say in what to grow or what to sell or what to eat! Engaging them at every turn is important if you expect them to follow in your footsteps. It is a delicate balance!

Also, everything is not about the work. Have some fun. It is a farm, so take time to go exploring or to enjoy early morning or evening walks. The daylight will burn away anyway. Yes, you need to get what you need to get done, but remember to live too!

Besides thinking about who is following behind, think about who has led the way for you. Don't shut out the grandparents or other seasoned family members, or even brothers, sisters, and cousins. There is so much knowledge and experience that resides in each of them. Utilize, encourage, and actively nurture those relationships. You may need them, and they might also need to be connected to your farm. Allowing their pride to shine is an integral part of the story. Their sphere of influence is different than yours and their connections and what they know may prove helpful at some point. Additionally, sometimes several extra hands go a long way!

There are some interesting statistics coming out that indicate there could be a major shift in family farm management coming up. As the current farmers continue to age and retire, their children or heirs appear to have a different point of view as to what the family farm should be going forward. I have read numerous articles about sons and

The next generation of farmers seems more willing to talk risks, do things differently, and farm in ways that will hopefully begin to to heal the land.

daughters in their forties taking ownership of the family farm and not wishing it to be a place for growing conventional crops, at least not on the large scale. Small-scale farming, especially by women, seems to be the fastest growing sector of agriculture currently. There is hope! That is also one important reason I wanted to share all of these experiences. So many of us are coming from non-farming backgrounds. How in the world can we take this on? I read too that folks in their fifties are often very successful in their encore careers and are inclined to do more in the way of community building and work that resonates with their sense of purpose. Farming offers that too! To that end, I hope that all these words ring true with you. Make sure you use the resource pages and online links. Utilize all the tools you have at your disposal. Most of all, share your vision with your family.

American Culture

— Greg Wade, Baker at Publican Breads, Chicago

A society's culture is demonstrated by the way a people interact with each other and the world around them through mediums such as art, music, and cuisine. It could even be defined as the demonstration of a people's relationship with the world. American culture has consistently been thought of as a conglomeration of the different cultures that have come to this land, without any distinct characteristics of its own. Compare this to a society with a strong heritage, such as France or Italy, and a very specific set of crops and cooking techniques come to mind. Those cultures have been developing a relationship with their lands for millennia and it is that relationship and the subsequent culture that could explain why a people did things a certain way. Before there was refrigeration, they needed to preserve meat for the winter and created duck confit and prosciutto. Summer brings abundance and heat, so cool dishes with fresh fruits and vegetables like berry salads and gazpacho became popular.

When colonists settled in America, there seemed to be an infinite amount of land to cultivate, from which the idea evolved that developing a relationship with the land was unnecessary. We brought crops, farming techniques, and animals from our homelands and tried to impose them upon this new settlement. When the current land's resources were depleted, we moved west. Eventually this limitless land had boundaries and we began to understand just how much of a problem we had created by depleting our soils. As an American people, we are now developing a relationship with our land and our food; we are now creating our own culture. It is for us to decide, with much awareness and very deliberate intentions—because this is no small feat—what our culture looks like. Because our heritage has such variety, the emerging culture is boundless. We don't hold ourselves to strict rules. We can use French cooking techniques with Latin American flavors. America deserves a culture as strong and diverse as its heritage, and the way to achieve that is through our choices, our actions, and our relationship with our farmland and our food.

Cash or Barter
Farmers have much to be thankful for, including being able to provide healthy food for their own families, the satisfaction that comes from serving others, and learning how to get by on just what they need.

CHAPTER 8

Getting By on More

Being More Resourceful

I can hear you now: "What is this? I thought we were going to have to give up a pile of stuff in order to make this work. I figured the chapter title was going to be 'Getting By on Less!' But you say 'more?'"

Yep, I do. Give me a few minutes here to explain.

Let's start by having you make a list of all the things you are thankful for that didn't cost you any money. And actually, try to do that at the beginning of each new year. I find it is quite amazing to think about all the things that we are thankful or grateful for. I believe it also transfers into the rest of our relationships. Just this past Thanksgiving season, I sent out the regular Friday email to our chef community expressing our gratitude for all their support and encouragement this past season. The response we had back from so many of our chef friends was a bit overwhelming. We even heard from chefs who have since moved away and are no longer able to purchase from us, all expressing gratitude for what they had experienced in their time with us and sharing stories of thankfulness in their situations where they are today. Don't underestimate the power of gratitude!

Feed Your Family First

If all goes well, you will be producing a lot of food. You must feed yourself and your family first! I mean that emphatically! I know of a number of farmers who sell everything they produce and then go to the grocery store and buy their family's vegetables or meat there. What? You are growing some of the absolute finest products and you aren't eating them or feeding them to your family? We have this huge opportunity to have the best. Please don't waste that. Freeze, can, dehydrate, eat everything that you can. Knock your food budget down as low as you can. Grow things that your family is excited about eating. Make time to preserve all you can. And, really, feed yourselves first!

Find Free Resources

Next, as you work on this dream farm of yours, you must learn to acquire new resources. I read a great article a number of years ago that I still think about. It talked about beginning a farm with no money: https://smallfarmersjournal.com/how-to-get-into-farming-with-no-money/. The basic notion is to begin with a mentor and to learn as much as you can from that mentor. YouTube is great, but having someone you can work alongside is invaluable. There are a lot of other important concepts, so take a look!

Save Seeds & Preserve Legacies

Here are a few other things to help you get by. Save seed! We plant nearly 100 percent heirloom varieties of grain and vegetables. We save our own seed from our corn, wheat, rye, sorghum, potatoes, tomatoes, peppers, beans, peas, and more. The crops have acclimated to our farm and our climate. We grow one particular variety of pepper from Mexico. When we planted them the first year, barely any matured before the first frost. Now, several years later, they are acclimated, and we now are getting ripe peppers before the average first frost. As time has gone by, yields have increased, as well as the quality of the crop. Saving that seed frees us from having to purchase seed each year. Also, some of those crops are really hard to find seed for. We were able to get a start of specific varieties from kind people all over the world, but we've had to save our own in order to continue to grow those same varieties. We have also passed some of those seeds on to others, either in trade or in donation. In the resource section I list several good books on seed saving as well as sources to get you started.

Speaking of saving seed, several years ago we received a letter in the mail from a distant cousin, asking if we still grew Kickapoo beans. We had no idea what they were referring to. So we asked and were told the story of the first winter that Valentine Martin Darnall came to this land. During that winter, the native Kickapoo came from their village to check on him and his family. The Kickapoo had brought with them a parcel of dried bean seeds. According to our cousin, Grandfather Darnall saved some of those seeds and planted them the following spring. Amazingly, those seeds have been passed down and planted through the generations. Our cousin sent us a sack of them and now we are growing them again on the land that they were grown on prior to our family's arrival.

The story doesn't end there. We did a couple of other things. First, we sent some of the seeds, along with the story, to the seed vault in Svalbard, Norway. Second, we returned them full circle from where they had come. The Kickapoo have a biennial powwow in our area that is open to the public. In talking with our cousin that had shared the seed with us, we decided to take a package of the bean seeds to the Kickapoo. After all these years, the elders were unaware of the bean story, but they were intensely interested in having the seeds and the tradition of planting them restored. This was a most amazing experience. This is getting by on more!

Bartering Still Works

Barter and trade! It is a bit amazing at times to stop and look at the things we acquire. We have traded goods for labor or other goods a number of times with other farmers. Develop community! Develop relationships! One amazing resource that Will has discovered is the Allis Chalmers forum (you know, like the tractors), which we like to think of as an online coffee shop we can visit to share ideas and seek knowledge from online mentors. If Will ever has a question about most anything he can shoot it out to the folks on the forum and have an answer or ten back in a matter of a few minutes. If he is in the middle of taking a tractor apart and replacing a part and doesn't quite know how it goes, they have an answer and can walk him through it. If he needed a used part, somebody has it for him. He posted a question about old barns the other day, and wow—that got everyone reminiscing and sharing their thoughts and pictures of barns that mean a lot to them. A community! He has made that forum of folks a great resource.

Build a Lifestyle 2.0

I also believe we need to rethink the lifestyle that we wish to have. I know there are those that wish for a lot of material things and end up having to adjust their lifestyle to match their income. I challenge you to adjust your income to match your lifestyle! Being a farmer, you are essentially self-employed and responsible for creating income. Set goals. I think it is okay to say, "I need to create this much income to get by." But then hold your lifestyle to that level. If you end up exceeding that goal, don't go adjusting the lifestyle right away. Sock that extra away. Give yourself cushions!

Remember, we are at the whim of Mother Nature, and some years it can get rough! When you get a good yield, put some extra back for later. As you grow and build your farm and its production, invest in the farm's future, in your future! But do it wisely, with intention and purpose. You want to get to the place of less stress and worry. You want to get to the realization that the abundance is happening.

Be a Business Person

I remember hearing Joel Salatin give a talk several years ago. He said a lot of things that evening, but one thing I remember was that we as farmers need to dress and act like the business people that we are. There is no need to go to town looking like you just crawled out from changing the oil on the tractor. I know sometimes you have to go for a part and it just isn't convenient to change clothes in order to run and get an oil filter. I am guilty of this as much as anyone, but there is validity in what Joel was saying.

If we are going to be successful, we need to look successful. We need to speak successful words. No negative thoughts or words. Represent your farm as an important business in the community, because it is! People want to see and relate and spend time with successful folks. People want to support success. If we portray that image, we not only have that reflected back on us; it also reflects on other small farmers. We as a tribe need to support each other and re-enforce the vision of sustainable, successful, small-scale family farms.

Tell Your Story

So, when you develop your story or your narrative, keep all of this in mind. Not that you should use hyperbole, but keep it positive, moving forward. Keep it real. Allow people to see your dream. Listen to others—sometimes they are looking for a way to live vicariously through you. There are lots of folks who wish they could be in your shoes. They are the romantics. Heck, that may be you right now, wishing and hoping you had a farm and were living the dream.

Just remember then, when you do get there, that there will be a good number of folks coming behind you, watching and wishing. Be real, be positive, and be encouraging. Be truthful and be willing to share your experience. By doing so, you are increasing your sphere of influence and also the number of folks who are looking to farm with purpose! This is a very good thing!

Here's another idea for you. Develop your own story. In most every small community there are opportunities for you to share your dream and your experiences. There are numerous civic organizations looking for presenters for their monthly meetings. Here are a few that we have spoken to over the years: Rotary International, Chamber of Commerce, 4H, Future Farmers of America (FFA), homemaker's clubs, historical societies, retired teacher's associations, homeschool groups, high school agriculture classes, university classes, permaculture workshops, and probably several dozen more. All of them are interested in what you have to say and why you are making these kinds of choices. Learn to tell a good story, and learn to tell it with passion, commitment, honesty, and vulnerability. Realize that everyone you speak to is a potential customer; treat them well and with respect. Once you get comfortable with this new-found person trying to reside inside you, share your passion so that it helps to build your business. The abundance will follow!

Stella Natura

Working with Cosmic Rhythms
Biodynamic Planting Calendar

2020
Inspiration & Practical Advice for
Gardeners & Professional Growers

Biodynamic Calendar

*Learning to work in harmony with Mother Nature has
made a significant difference for many of our crops.*

CHAPTER 9

Planning the Season: All of Them

From Cover Crops to Starters to Harvest, It's All about Logistics

I am writing this chapter on New Year's Eve and it is 2°F outside! What a great time to have a cup of hot tea, sit in front of the fire, and dream about the upcoming planting season. You need to know that your farm will probably never look any better than it does right now—the image you have in your head this time of year! Once the season begins and reality sets in, the landscape changes! I think the winter is a natural time to reflect on the past season and to think about the ways we can improve in the coming year. But what if you haven't had that experience yet? What if you are just now planning for your first rodeo? Well, then, let's figure this out.

Do you remember what I said at the beginning about starting small? That still applies. A good general rule of thumb is that one person can usually take care of one acre of garden or crop somewhat comfortably without a lot of equipment. An acre is 43,560 square feet, or close to an area of 200 feet by 200 feet. We make most of our vegetable rows 200 feet long; you can see the end of the row that way.

An acre of any one crop has the potential to produce a large amount of product. John Kempf of Advancing Eco Agriculture says that the genetic potential of one acre of tomatoes is approximately 120,000 pounds! I am not advocating planting your whole acre into tomatoes, but think about what you plan to plant and remember to have an idea of where it is going.

If you have done some of your homework ahead of the spring planting season, you should have an idea of what you will be growing and how much. Diversity is really important here. Being able to offer a good array of vegetables and/or fruit throughout the season will allow you to maximize your cash flow and keep your face in front of your customers throughout the year. Getting in early, staying consistent, and being there late is most ideal. We now are able to deliver fifty out of fifty-two weeks each year, taking Christmas and New Year's weeks off.

In the beginning, we started all of our transplants downstairs in the basement under grow lights. All the brassicas, tomatoes, peppers, and early vine crops were begun in six-packs in what are called 10-by-20 trays. We have since outgrown that room and our set up. We now have one of our Down at the Farms farmers custom grow all our starts in their large commercial greenhouse. We supply the seed, any organic starter solutions, and the timing we wish to transplant, and they do the rest. They now start thousands of kale, cabbage, brussels sprouts, parsley, celery, celeriac, tomato, pepper, and herb transplants for us. Then we are able to pick them up and move them into the field at the right time and the transplants are in prime condition.

Many of the seed catalogs have yield information as to what to expect in, for example, a 100-foot row. Using some of that data, we can estimate how much of each crop we need to produce for our chefs' needs. We make a field map each year and rotate crops through that production area. We try not to have the same family of crop follow in that space. So, we wouldn't plant tomatoes following potatoes or cabbage following kale. Many times we try to follow a root crop with a leafy crop. Different crops affect the soil's structure and nutrient composition. Tomatoes and peppers are heavy feeders and use quite a bit of phosphorous and potassium. Many of the root crops will bring nutrients from deeper in the soil to the surface and make any excess available in the following crop.

As you plan, think about plant size. Make sure you have enough space for those tomatoes to grow and fill out. What looks like a lot of space in May can be way too crowded come August when those plants are going crazy! Also think about where you plant what. You don't want to plant your sweet corn on the south side of a row of peppers or something that needs full sun. The corn could cast shade on that smaller crop and, additionally, the roots may take away some of the nutrients from nearby plants.

Your planting plan should also take companion planting into consideration. There are whole books written on this. Check a few of them out and learn which plants do best with what neighbors and which do not. Sunflowers, for instance, have what is called an allelopathic effect—that they exude compounds from their roots that have a limiting effect on other plants' growth. Similarly, some herbs have the power to keep away certain insect pests. Remember that everything is connected and learn to use that connectedness.

Make notes—lots of them. Observe what is going on: weather conditions, soil temperature, returning or migrating birds, the first bumblebee, and more. Tune into the world around you, as you are part of it. All of this awareness will come in handy as you grow in your position of steward of your land. Pay attention to your crops as they emerge. This is one of their most vulnerable times. Keep them free of weed pressure if you can. Get them off to a good start now and the reward will be there when it is time for harvest. Keep notes about your planting, weeding, cultivating, and harvest. As time goes on you will have your own journal of your farm. You will be better able to understand the best times for managing your crops.

What Is Biodynamics?

Let's talk about the best time to manage crops. We have been making use of the biodynamic calendars for the last dozen or more years. We like the *Stella Natura* calendar, available from Acres U.S.A. It gives the best planting cultivation, grafting, and harvesting times each month. Learning to work in concert with these biodynamic forces has made a significant difference for many of our crops. We actually use the monthly pages in the biodynamic calendar as our crop management journal, recording when we plant, cultivate or harvest a crop. Saving these calendars and referencing them over the course of years helps us develop a history and a pattern that works for us. You can see the resource section for more information on biodynamics, but here are a few guiding principles we've adopted.

Biodynamics is a regenerative agriculture "system," holistic in approach and practice. It is based on the work of Rudolph Steiner (1861–1925). Through observation and many trials, several key concepts emerged. Without getting in too deep, I want to share some of the practical timing and crop management techniques.

Full Moon

The **full moon** tends to be a good time for planting seed and applying any foliar sprays. It typically is a time of greater moisture. Full moon is usually associated with more issues of fungal disease. With the increased moisture we can tend to have a better chance of frost. Full moon is also a good time to deworm livestock.

New Moon

New moon is a period to harvest grain crops or cut firewood. There tend to be fewer moisture influences and our grain crops will dry down quicker. Also, this is a good time for castrating animals, as there tends to be less bleeding.

Ascending Period

During the **ascending period**—when the moon is rising in its phase from new moon to full—we see increased seed growth. This is also a great time to graft trees or tap maple trees.

Descending Time

During the **descending time**, the period between full and new, on the waning side, we do our transplanting, pruning, or cultivating.

Perigee

Perigee is the period when the moon is closest to the earth in its orbit. This time will have influences similar to a full moon. It is a good time to plant potatoes, if you wish to have a lot of smaller ones.

Apogee

Conversely, **apogee** is when the moon is farthest from the earth. This will have influences similar to a new moon and is a great time to plant potatoes if you want larger tubers.

Carrots seem to have their highest yields when planted just before a full moon. Radishes and potatoes have their highest yields when planted in the moon's third quarter. Peas and beans in the first quarter.

Most crops will have their highest yields when they are planted when the moon is closest to the earth (perigee).

It is best not to irrigate two days before a full moon or two days after, or at perigee. This can increase the potential for fungal diseases.

Breeding livestock at apogee tends to produce more male offspring. Breeding at perigee tends to produce more females.

I will stop there. These observations and tendencies have been observed in more than 100 years research. This is not the only way we run our farm, but we do try to utilize as many of these tools and influences as we can. Sometimes it works with our schedule and Mother Nature, sometimes it doesn't. But as we have farmed, we have noticed definite trends. Besides, it is pretty fun!

Something that most of us don't think about is the fact that we need to keep planting! If the crop you are planting has a short window of growth and then harvest (i.e., lettuce, radishes, and beets), we should plant again in about ten days to two weeks so we can have a continual supply coming on. You might be able to harvest your radishes for a few days once they are the perfect size, but then they can become too hot, too pithy, or even go to seed and no longer be good radish roots. And if your goal was to have radishes for six weeks, you are sunk after the first week. So, keep planting! One other aside: if your radishes do start to flower, did you know that the flowers are edible? Also, the immature seed pods that form after the flowers are edible and delicious. Learn to utilize all of the stages of edibility of each of your crops. Not all parts are edible, but learn which are and make use of those as another crop to market!

Likewise, late summer is another important planting season. We typically plant our fall carrots toward the end of June or the first of July and sow fall radishes, rutabagas, and turnips around the first half of August. Fall crops are wonderfully sweet and have the advantage of less weed pressure, less bug pressure, and often less competition from other farmers growing produce. Many folks just run out of steam or interest by September and are winding down. The fall season is one of our favorites! The roots are sweeter, as any hint of frost sends the sugars in the plant into the root to keep it from freezing. Another big plus is that the fall root crops like rutabagas, turnips, potatoes, and radishes have a much better ability to be stored longer term under the correct conditions. We have kept watermelon radishes and green meat radishes in the walk-in cooler all the way through the spring from a November harvest. They were perfectly solid, sweet, spicy, and delicious.

Another crop we do a lot of is squash. We grow them mainly for the squash blossoms. Our chefs often order several thousand blossoms each week. We plant the first planting toward the end of April. Over the last ten years or more, our first date of blossom harvest has fallen on the week of June 24. We sell the blossoms for $0.40 to $0.50 each and try to have at least two to three plantings so we can have blossoms all the way till frost. We have found that we have two favorite varieties. First is the New England Pie pumpkin for the size and sheer number of blossoms produced. The second is a variety from Italy called Long of Naples. We have one chef who uses that for stuffing as the blossoms are sometimes six to eight inches long! We harvest blossoms typically on Monday and Tuesday ahead of the Wednesday delivery. We begin about 6 a.m., when the blossoms are just beginning to open. We want to have all of them picked before 7:30 a.m., as they will begin to fade at that point and the quality will suffer. We pick only the male blossoms. The female blossoms have the beginnings of a squash or pumpkin on the stem end; this is how you tell the difference. There are some chefs who love the female ones too. But there are many more male blossoms, as they begin flowering sometimes a week or two before the females. I believe that it is the squash's way of drawing in the pollinators ahead of the female blossoms appearing and needing to be pollinated to produce a squash with viable seed. We really don't care if we get the actual squash, as we will have made way more money on this crop of blossoms than on the squash itself. But, don't forget, it does take some nutrition to keep these plants healthy and robust. For example, did you know that you can influence the ratio of male-to-female blossoms based on the availability of phosphorous? If you want more male blossoms, feed less P; if you want more squash, feed more P and zinc, to help make P more available. We do try to do a planting of squash about thirty days apart from the April planting through June or the first half of July. Once we get into the middle of July, it is somewhat iffy if we are going to have enough time to get the last planting to size and flowering before the weather turns colder and the daylight hours diminish.

Another consideration as you are continuing your harvest through the season is to keep the soil covered. By this I mean that if you harvest a crop and aren't planning to replant until, say, August, plant a cover crop on it. Buckwheat or oats might be a good idea. You want to continue to feed that soil biology all the time. Buckwheat is fantastic at loosening the soil and at drawing in beneficial insects. Don't let the buckwheat or oats go to seed, but allow them to grow and scavenge nutrients and then make them available for the next crop. You could mow or till them in at least a couple weeks ahead of your replanting. That way the cover crop can begin to break down and not tie up the nutrients or the biology for the succeeding crop. Then, in the fall, as you are taking out your crops, again think about planting some type of cover. Fall tillage radishes mixed with oats are super. Both of them will winter kill and leave behind their nutrients for the crop you plant in the spring. Just try to get them planted before the end of August if you can.

If you aren't planning to do a cover crop or are unable to do so, leaving the previous crop's vegetative debris on the soil has some benefit. While there are differing points of view on this, we tend to try to leave our soil covered in some way over the winter. We don't want any erosion if we can help it, and we want to be able to protect the biology in the soil with that cover. Another aspect is weed control. If at the end of the season we were to till all of the areas, we would be tilling into the soil any of the weed seed that was produced. If we leave that above ground, even mowing it down would be fine; this then allows all kinds of elements to work on destroying that weed seed. Everything from rodents and birds, insects, and even the freezing and thawing cycle can break down those seeds and keep them from being the raging nuisance they could be if we had tilled them in. I realize there are times that this system doesn't make perfect sense, but I felt it is something you should know.

So in your planning, think about your ability to feed your crops. We do a foliar feed using the nutritional products each week. We scout or walk the crops every few days to observe what is going on. If you are cultivating, you want to do this just as any new weeds are just emerging. Waiting until they have two or three leaves on them is really too late and they may be taking nutrition away from your crop.

Learn to recognize the different insects. There are good ones and ones that like to eat what you are growing. If you can refer to the plant health chapter again and understand more about boosting that plant's immunity, the pressure from pests and disease will be far less impactful.

Continue to keep notes and record your harvest dates and yields. There are many programs for record keeping. Utilize a system that works for you and that you can use and update easily. You want to be able to access this info for your planning purposes but also to use for charting your sales to your markets. If you can create an availability chart or seasonality calendar, it will go a long way in helping to plan for the next season. You will be better able to fill the gaps or work to extend the season for specific crops. Also, keep notes to help you better understand the profitability of your crops. Some crops are more profitable than others. Figure out what is most profitable for you.

Then focus harder on marketing the most profitable. Sweet corn takes up a lot of space, time, and nutrients, for a one-time harvest. Not only that, but during sweet corn season, it seems like lots of folks have it to sell. You may find that field space is better suited to another crop or crops. Or figure out a specific sweet corn that is so totally different and exciting that no one else is growing. Find a specific market just for that and make that your signature item.

Plan to make progress. You don't have to be perfect. You don't have to have perfect-looking fields or a perfect farm. Just work to make progress. Celebrate the small accomplishments as well as the big ones. Try to hit your goals, and don't be devastated if you come up short. Figure out what the limiting factors might be. Work on those and try to do better going forward. Planning is a really important part of your progress. I wrote success first, but success is measured in many different ways, and I want you to measure progress, which is much more realistic. Even now, after almost fifteen years, I like to think we are still making progress. I also think we still have more to go in order to be able to move this farm forward. Makes me ask myself, do we want to be known only as successful farmers or as progressive farmers? Both would be good, but I will take making progress any day.

Henry,
shown in the photo above
with Will, loves this tractor.

CHAPTER 10

Farm Hands

Matt and Annie created the documentary *Sustainable*, which was filmed at the farm for nearly three calendar years. Their son, Henry, became one of our "farm hands" during the course of the filming. Henry, shown in the photo above with Will, loves this tractor!

I want to explore something else with you: the meaning of farm hands. This past year, we have had the honor and pleasure of participating in a monthly farm dinner series at a restaurant called The Heritage in Forest Park, Illinois. One of the themes for the dinners was "Farm Hands." We decided to serve chicken produced by two high school brothers, Jeremy and Justin Steffen from Millie's Corner Farm. They are also farm hands for us at Spence Farm. The dinner theme started with highlighting their contributions to the weekly deliveries making it to the restaurant and their help as our farm hands.

What really came to be understood from that dinner was the many meanings of the term "farm hands." Going back to the earlier history of Spence Farm, there were multiple families living and working here; some were family, and some were tenants. It took many hands to do the work that was required back then. During the 1940s there was a family of eight who lived upstairs in the big house and provided much of the needed labor in addition to the family. Today, Jeremy and Justin, along with a few other folks and volunteers, help with much of the extra hand work that needs to be done.

So, we talked in between courses about the history of farm hands and how today it is still somewhat that way on our farm. We also explored how much of the food we eat, especially vegetables and fruit, still have a good amount of hand work required to get it to the consumer. However, we talked about the difference between that hand-harvested food and the more conventional farmers that surround us today. For them, there is much less hand work. Their seed is treated with fungicides and so, for the most part, is not touched. It goes into their planters and is planted into the ground, possibly using GPS tracking. Any fertilizer or chemical applications are made by large spray rigs or by airplanes. The harvest is done with massive combines and augured into wagons and then into semi-trucks and taken to the elevator to be loaded onto rail cars to some faraway destination. Really, I am not sure that the corn or bean crop ever has any hands touching it!

That made us think about comparing that scenario with ours. Let's take our corn crop for a comparison. We begin by putting our saved seed in bags. We add in a microbial inoculant and stir it around by hand. We hand-pour the seed into the planter and then plant it into the field. Our tractor that we use to pull the planter is from the early 1960s and, in order to plant a straight row, it requires the operator to drive straight. This is part of the art of farming. We don't have any GPS equipment. I'm not saying that GPS is bad; I'm saying that it doesn't fit our farm mo del.

Many times, we check for germination about a week later, digging in the soil to see how the seed is doing. Once the corn is up, we cultivate it at least three times and sometimes walk and pull weeds by hand. Next, we will hand-harvest some of the immature ears and sell as baby corn. We allow the rest of the corn to mature, but we still check it as it nears maturity, stripping back the husk and seeing how it looks. Many times, we will then walk through the field and hand-harvest the best-looking ears to save for our seed for the next year. We run those ears by hand through a hand-cranked corn sheller before storing it in a bag for use the following spring. The rest of the crop is harvested using equipment, but then cleaned and bagged before we pour it through our stone mill, which turns it into cornmeal or grits. I know that sounds like a lot of hand work, and it is. But let's think about something else too.

Do you recall a time when someone came up behind you and placed their hand on your shoulder or on your back? Can you remember the feeling that you experienced with that? Or how about when someone you care about touches your arm or hand and that transfer of good energy or vibe comes through? I believe that same energy transfer happens when we do our hand work with our food crops. We are imparting something from us into that product. THEN, to follow this further, we harvest our produce—by hand we wash it, bag it, label it, and then deliver it to the kitchens at the restaurants. Next, they take it and wash it, prepare it, plate it, and serve it. The number of times that caring hands have put energy into that food is quite amazing.

Something else that reminds me of "hands" is when we are in the kitchen at The Heritage. When the plates of food are ready to be served the expediter calls, "HANDS," asking for a server to deliver it to the diner's table. Now that is the ultimate send-off!

As we have grown on our farm, we have needed extra hands, extra people. Finding good help is sometimes really a challenge, but we have been extremely fortunate. We have also worked hard to make our helpers feel empowered and responsible. They feel a sense of pride and they "own" the work they do here. We give them meaningful work and try to explain that the work has purpose. They get it!

So, as you work with your hands, take care of them. Farms are not the safest environments and things can happen quickly. You need your hands, all of them! You need to remember to allow that good energy to flow into your product. You shouldn't feel bad about doing hand work. It is important and rewarding.

Troy-Bilt Tiller
This is our first tiller. In the
beginning, try to get by
the best you can with
what you already own
or can easily borrow.

CHAPTER 11

Equipment
From Humble Beginnings

Remember what I said about starting small? This chapter will chronicle our small beginnings. Above is the Troy-Bilt tiller that we began with. Our gardens were relatively small at that time. We started with this and saved and worked up the next year. Equipment can be expensive, but it can also be inexpensive. Starting out, we knew we couldn't afford new and expensive equipment. Heck, we didn't really know exactly what we needed. And many times, as we gained more experience, we realized our needs were changing. So, I would say, think hard about what equipment you think you need.

In the beginning, get by the best you can with what you have or can borrow or share. At first, we even considered whether we could do horse or oxen power. We didn't consider that too long, as we just didn't feel that was a good fit for us. But for others, it could be!

As we became more involved and began pricing certain pieces, we realized that sometimes brand matters. We noticed that John Deere tractors were pretty popular, but that a tractor with the same horsepower by Allis Chalmers or International was a fraction of the cost. Also, my grandpa had nearly all Allis Chalmers equipment when he was farming. So, overall, that is what we have gone back to.

We also have sought out the older, smaller-sized tractors and implements. We now have an Allis Chalmers 7060, which Will was able to purchase for an outstanding price, as well as an Allis Chalmers combine. We made those purchases based on the evolution of our needs as a farm. In the beginning, we didn't have use for anything that size, but as we have grown, our market for whole wheat, rye, and cornmeal has increased the small plots to small acres. Utilizing a combine with a twelve-foot grain head helps to speed up our wheat harvest tremendously compared to the five-foot model of the Allis Chalmers All Crop. However, we didn't make that switch until we knew we had the market and the need. Make sense?

As with relationships and livestock, so with equipment. If you have it, you have maintenance issues. Learn to deal with it and learn to do as much of it as you can yourself. Utilizing the older equipment comes with the probability of increased maintenance, but also with the reality that that older equipment is much easier to work on. This is where Will shines. He not only makes good use of his community on the Allis Chalmers Forum, but he has mentors in the community he can ask questions of or go to for advice. He also can usually "see" the solution to many things.

Take care of your equipment! Grease it, change the oil, keep things sharpened, cleaned, and well taken care of and they will last you a long time.

Let me give you a pictorial review of some of our equipment, then and now. Hopefully it will spark some ideas for you.

This is our first three-point tiller.

Here is the first three-point tiller we had. The old Ford loader tractor belongs to our neighbor and has been on loan to us for the last 20 years or more! We purchased the attached tiller from another friend for about $800 and it worked really well. We finally wore it out and had to purchase a new one several years ago. The tractor still resides here and is used occasionally. This is something that we hinted at earlier in a previous chapter. Sometimes neighbors have equipment that they either don't use any longer or just don't need and wish to send it somewhere besides the scrap dealer. We have been the joyful recipient of several pieces like that.

1944 Allis Chalmers Model C Tractor

This was our first real tractor of our own! It is a 1944 Allis Chalmers Model C. Here Kris and Will are planting potatoes using an old horse-drawn potato planter that was given to the farm by another friend.

Here is another picture of the potato planter. It is now pulled by our Allis Chalmers D15. With this planter we can plant a few thousand pounds of seed potatoes in a morning. It works well. We have also used it to plant garlic on occasion.

Potato Planter
now pulled by
our Allis Chalmers
D15Tractor

A single-row, horse-drawn cultivator

Early on, we didn't have any tillage tools but the small Troy-Bilt and a hoe! We were able to purchase this single-row, horse-drawn cultivator at a local farm sale. Keeping on the potato theme, Kris and Will are cultivating potatoes as they emerge. We used this cultivator for a couple seasons and then passed it onto another young farmer, who we think still makes use of it.

Allis Chalmers Model G Tractor

Following in the wheel tracks of the horse-drawn cultivator is this Allis Chalmers Model G. We use this tractor about every week during the growing season. We use it for planting, with two people—one sitting on the front and pushing an Earthway planter to plant tons of our vegetable crops. We also use it for cultivating and hilling of potatoes and numerous other crops. These little tractors were the hot thing in the 50s and 60s. This one is from 1949. We paid about $3,000 for it and several attachments.

*Horse-drawn
potato digger*

One day on the way back home from deliveries in Chicago, Kris and I took a different side road home. As we passed by a farmhouse, my head jerked around when I noticed this old, horse-drawn potato digger. We stopped and inquired about it, and it belonged to the brother of a friend of ours. I called him, and he said it was ours as long as we didn't take it to the scrap guy! We used it up until the last year or two. It made digging potatoes a lot easier; it just didn't make picking them up any easier, as you had to still follow behind and pick up the potatoes in the row. See the next photo for the next evolution.

Potato digger

This one works great! It does take about five people to run it efficiently: four on the back and the tractor driver! This is made by U.S. Small Farm Equipment. Two people can ride on it on each side, and as the conveyor shuttles the potatoes from the front blade to the back, the pickers just snatch the potatoes and place them in 5-gallon buckets that are set into holders near the back platform. This does take a chase truck or tractor with a wagon to empty the buckets quickly. But it still is much faster than the previous model!

Allis Chalmers Model 7060 Tractor

Never, ever, did we think we needed or would get a tractor this large, but we sure have used it and continue to be happy with its purchase. Will was able to buy this tractor from another farmer about an hour away for $5,000. We use it for pulling a disc, pulling the field cultivator, and also pulling the potato harvester in the previous picture. It has way more power than we really need, but the price was very good and, honestly, it should last us for years!

Earthway Seeder

We have a couple of these fairly inexpensive Earthway seeders. They come with different seed plates and can plant everything from lettuce to sweet corn and beans. They are not perfect, but they get the job done!

Two-row John Deere Planter

This two-row John Deere planter was given to us by a retiring farmer who kept it to plant his sweet corn. We have planted corn, peas, beans, and the like. With enough different plates, I believe you could plant almost any vegetable crop.

Four-row John Deere Planter

In this picture you'll see that we are getting bigger: a four-row John Deere planter! This one was similar to the previous planter, but with two more rows. We are currently trading up to a John Deere 7000 four-row planter that will do a better job of accurately planting our corn and dry beans. This one here has planted many acres in its time, and we paid a whopping $125 for it!

*Single-row Corn Picker
from New Idea*

For several years we hand-harvested our Iroquois White Corn. We then moved up to this single-row corn picker from New Idea. We paid about $1,700 for it and we thought we were really something then! Today, we still use this picker, especially to pick the Iroquois that will get roasted before it gets shelled and milled into cornmeal. The wagon behind was a gift as well.

*175 lb. Capacity
Spreader or Seeder*

This is a small 175-pound capacity spreader or seeder. We have used it to broadcast oats, rye, clover, soil amendments, and such. We can pull it using the lawn mower. In small areas we drag a bed spring frame over the planted area with the lawn mower to cover the seed. This works well for planting the buffer strips on the end rows next to our neighbor's fields.

A step up from the previous spreader is this flare box wagon with an end gate seeder. As we increased the size of our small grain plantings, we used this to broadcast up to five acres of wheat or rye. We also used it to overseed the small grain plots in late winter with clover or alfalfa. In the fall, we take out the seeder and put in the back panel and harvest corn or grains into it. I think we paid about $200 for this.

Single Gang, Straight Disc

This is a single gang, straight disc we use to drag over the previously broadcast seed from the flare box wagon. It helps to cover the seed and keep the seed surface loose and friable for the seed to emerge. It was in the fence row between us and our neighbor. It was his uncle's and I don't think Tom ever used it. It took several days of greasing and loosening the discs in order to get this to operate.

**175 lb. Capacity
Spreader or Seeder**

The next evolution happened a couple years ago when Will was able to obtain two of these grain drills. He bought one for $400 and the other was free. Now we can fill the seed box, set it to the proper planting rate and drill our small grain seed, beans, pasture mix, or cover crops in one pass as it drills the seed into the ground and covers it with the chains on the back.

**Allis Chalmers
All Crop Combine**

Here is our first combine. It was owned by a local gentleman who had it in a parade in town and we happened to be looking for one for harvesting our small grain crops. Following the parade, we spoke with him about it and he said he was looking to sell it. We ended up purchasing it for a whopping $150, along with a mounted corn picker that we later traded for new wheel rims for another tractor. This Allis Chalmers All Crop can harvest over 100 different crops. It does an amazing job of cleaning the seed. It is slow, but really efficient.

The hopper on the Allis Chalmers All Crop Combine holds seventeen bushels

This is a photo of emptying the hopper on the combine into a wooden barge wagon. The hopper on the combine holds all of 17 bushels! So, on a good crop, emptying is pretty constant! Will is wearing the appropriate colored T-shirt too!

Hand-Built Transplant Planter.

This is a sample of farm creativity. Here we are planting kale transplants. The 16-horsepower garden tractor is hydrostatic, meaning it has a variable speed lever that helps it to go faster or slower. The implement on the back was built by Will following a visit to the junk yard. We found a random frame, a seat from a van, packing wheels from a junked planter and mounted a fourteen-gallon spray rig behind Will's seat. From that spray rig trickles a transplant fertilizer solution into the furrow. With this set up we can transplant thousands of seedlings in a short amount of time. Total cost for this without the spray unit, including paint, was about $65.

Utilizing things that most people discard, we made up a pull-behind water wagon that we use to water seedlings or trees. The steel wheels still work well!

This 1995 Ford Econoline diesel van was one of our delivery vans early on. We were also able to utilize the used vegetable oil from the restaurants as fuel. Our neighbor would take the used oil that we brought back each week, and he would filter it and turn it into biodiesel. He would give us a credit for all the oil we brought to him and then charge us a fair price for the fuel. Soon, though, we outgrew this van.

GMC Refrigerated Box Truck with Lift Gate

In the fall of 2016, we purchased this used GMC box truck with refrigeration and a lift gate on the back. It is our new delivery truck and we love it! And actually, one of our restaurants helped set up a GoFundMe page to help pay for the truck! After one full season of using this, we are nearly outgrowing it. We're thinking of purchasing a second truck and splitting our delivery route on Wednesdays. We were able to purchase this truck for about $8,000.

6' x 10' Hog Pen

Switching gears, this is one of the hog pens that we used to pasture our American Guinea Hogs. It is made from two sixteen-foot hog panels bent at right angles to make a pen of about six feet by ten feet. We cover the back end with an 8-foot by 10-foot tarp that gives shade and protection from wind, rain, and snow. More info on the pen is in the livestock section. Early on, we had just a few of these pens and could easily move them twice a day on pasture by hand.

Using a tractor to pull four hog pens at one time

As the number of pigs and pens increased, we had to become more efficient with our pig chores. Here we use our tractor hooked to a two-wheel wagon with the water tank for watering. We also installed a twelve-foot beam across the back with chains attached that we could hook to a series of four hog pens and pull all four at one time. We threaded a hickory pole through the pens to attach the chains to in order to pull all the pens simultaneously.

Hand-built Barrel Root Washer

Washing several hundred pounds of root crops each week causes someone like Will to come up with a better method. He didn't want to spend the money for a commercial barrel root washer, so we used some things around the farm and manufactured our own. The next winter, we hosted a barrel washer workshop at the farm and everyone went home with one.

That was a great day of community!

CHAPTER 12

Livestock
on Your Farm
A Serious Commitment

L et me begin this chapter with a couple of thoughts. First, I completely understand that livestock may or may not be your thing. I understand those who feel livestock belong on a farm and that there are differences of opinion. Remember, this is our experience we are sharing. No judgment calls either way, just information. To that end, we have learned a lot. And honestly, there is still a lot to learn.

Historically, our farm had livestock, as did most small family farms. During the history of the farm, there were chickens, hogs, sheep, cows, and horses. In the early years of homesteading, a family would have had livestock either for food, fiber, or power. Families would grow as much animal feed on the farm as possible so that they wouldn't have to rely on (and pay for) feed from somewhere else. In our family journals, Valentine Darnall brought along enough livestock from Kentucky to help ensure they would have meat and fiber to get them started here in Illinois.

We spent quite a bit of time discussing whether we would take on the responsibility of having animals on the farm. We talked about what kind of livestock, what breeds, how many, and what size animals. We talked about how we would raise them and for what purpose. We had conversations about how we would feed them and what was appropriate for the land, our time, and our experience. We ended up deciding that we wanted to focus on rare or endangered breeds, historical breeds. That seemed to fit the historic nature of our farm.

Focusing on heritage and endangered breeds has proved extremely meaningful on our historic farm.

Our first foray into returning livestock to our farm started while visiting friends of ours in Ohio. Judy and Skip had sheep called Jacob's Sheep. We ended up bringing two young ewes home with us. Jennie had four horns and Hannah had two. Their breed was listed on the American Livestock Breeds Conservancy list of rare or endangered breeds. As with any new endeavor, our first venture with livestock had its share of stress and doubts. There were so many unknowns. If you don't have any experience, everything is new or a crisis. You can read all you want, but in the end it boils down to you and the livestock in your care. With Jennie and Hannah, our pastures were different than what they had been used to and were much richer. Knowing nothing, it looked like they had a bit of bloat or gas from eating forage that was too rich. Talking with Judy and a local vet, we figured it out and were able to get them acclimated to their new environment. They survived! Hannah is now nearly fifteen years old; Jennie died this past summer. Both of the girls were spoiled to the hilt!

Over the last fifteen years, we have had the two Jacob's sheep, upwards of fifty American Guinea hogs, Narragansett turkeys, Black Cayuga ducks, numerous breeds of chicken and quail, Dexter cows, one Jersey calf, and two Black Angus steers. Except for the starter feed for the young poultry, we have produced all the feed for all our animals here on the farm. All our animals are pastured on our pastures. We feed the hogs, sheep, and cows our own hay in the wintertime, and they receive essentially no grain. Going this route has saved us a lot of money in feed cost and veterinary bills. Because our livestock has been on pasture and eating a diverse diet of grass and legumes, they have been extremely healthy.

Several years ago, we had a call from a farmer in Indiana that had a couple of American Guinea hogs. They were unable to continue to care for them, and they couldn't afford the feed. So a farmer friend who was looking for a couple hogs and I ended up purchasing a pregnant sow and another pair of young hogs. All had been fed GMO grain and were really agitated. We transported them home, and the next morning the sow had a litter of eleven piglets. She continued to be pretty hyper for some time, trying to jump out of her pen and running around like a racehorse! As quickly as we could, we began feeding her our alfalfa hay and reducing the grain. She began to settle down, and within a month or so she had calmed down considerably. This experience played out another time as well when we brought a new hog onto the farm. Once we took the grain out of their diet, the temperament changed a lot! We were convinced the grass-based diet was what we wanted for our livestock.

In the winter the hogs get our hay, and by April we are moving all of them out onto pasture. We move the hogs in their moveable pens twice a day. With that routine, they don't destroy the pasture unless it is exceedingly wet. Everyone stays on pasture until about the first of December, depending on the weather. Then we move all the pens up to the barnyard, arrange them side by side, bed them with straw, and surround the pens with straw bales to buffer the winter winds. Unless we get a massive blizzard, all the hogs are outside in their pens all winter. They can get shelter under their tarp covering and burrow down into the warm straw. Twice a day they get hay and fresh water.

We started with a young boar named Sam and a young gilt, or unbred female, named Swee. At about a year and a half we were able to put them together and Swee had her first litter three months, three weeks, and three days later, which is the gestation period for pigs. We also learned something interesting as things progressed. It seemed that we had better litters if we put our sows in with the boar about three to four days ahead of the full moon. We started to experiment with the biodynamic calendar that I talked about in a previous chapter. We wanted to try to raise several litters per year and sell some of the young piglets to other folks. The American Guinea hog's population in the mid-2000s had dropped to less than two hundred registered hogs left in the world. I don't remember every pig that we had, but by about 2014 we had nearly fifty to sixty hogs. We helped several other farmers throughout the Midwest get started raising them.

Our pastured pig infrastructure is simple, inexpensive, and mobile.

The sows farrow in their pens on pasture. We have had a small number of individual piglets lost from a mother laying on them, but very few. Many of our sows have been so docile that we could get in and make sure everyone was doing okay as she was having the piglets. Remember that saying about only wanting to work with nice folks? Same goes for your livestock. Don't keep the meanies. Having mean or really unpredictable livestock is not a good situation. Pay attention to all your animals. They are not pets, and you should respect that fact. Sometimes things happen and people can get hurt due to no real fault of the animal. We need to treat them with respect and have an awareness that things can sometimes go awry.

The American Guinea hog does not do well with a diet of all grain. They become exceedingly fat and end up with health issues. We wanted to have the hogs on grass for another reason too. We wanted to have the flavor of our farm come through in the flavor of the meat. And it does! Especially with pork, what you feed that animal in the last six weeks before slaughter gives the meat that specific undertone of flavor. We also realize that a grass-based diet gives those animals the good kind of omega fats, omega-3s. The omega-3 fatty acid is reportedly better for us than grain-based omega-6. In the fall, we also give the hogs pumpkins, apples, tomatoes, and any other field vegetables that are not getting sold or eaten by us. They love it too.

We have been very successful in farrowing American Guinea hogs on pasture.

Let me talk more about pastured animals and some of the benefits to having livestock on pasture. First, I believe it is a lot healthier for the animals. Cattle are herbivores—they eat plants. Their gut biome is based on that type of diet, and if they are fed a diet of grains, their gut bacteria changes dramatically.

Our small herd of cattle is rotated through about eight acres of mixed grasses and legumes. They get moved every day or two and we bring them fresh water twice a day. We basically have the eight acres broken into about half-acre paddocks. When it is time to move, we just drop a wire between the paddocks and everyone walks into the new area, anxious for the first fresh bite. The fence is electrified and for the most part is respected! In the winter, they are all moved up to an area outside our big barn and fed with our alfalfa hay. They have shelter if they choose to use it and are not on any concrete. We allow that area to grow out during the year, so they have some grazing to do once they are moved onto it. For the most part, they have done well and have not ended up in a mud hole. Keeping a good place for them to stay dry and clean has helped keep them healthy.

Breeding our cows is done by artificial insemination. We have Matt or Paul, from the local dairy down the road, come down whenever we wish to breed. We try to time the calf birth in May through August. That timeframe seems to work well for us as it is warmer, and the calf also has time to put on some weight before the onset of cold winter weather. In the beginning, Will would milk our cow and bottle feed the calf in order to make the calf really tame. Our first steer we had was extremely well behaved. We worked with him to lead, much like you would train an ox. He did well with voice commands and loved the extra attention. Ultimately, he still ended up in our freezers, but that experience was really valuable for us, as we learned how to handle our larger animals.

The chickens are treated about the same as the hogs and cows. We do feed the chickens and ducks our own wheat, rye, and any corn screenings from getting the corn cleaned, but only during the winter months. Once spring begins, they get let out of their coop and are totally free range on the farm. Many times, they head out to the cow pasture and scratch through the pasture looking for worms and bugs after the cows have grazed an area. They are eating grass and weeds throughout the farm. We save a lot of money on chicken feed and the chickens are doing us a favor in eating a lot of the bugs. Their egg yolks are the deepest orange you can imagine. Fantastic flavor too. We have also had a couple of hens live to be eleven to thirteen years old, still laying a few eggs per week. Pretty amazing!

Our chickens are 100 percent free range during the summer, even scavenging for their own food.

Having animals on pasture also benefits our land in many ways. It can increase carbon sequestration, increase microbial activity in the soil, increase soil fertility, and raise the quality of soil structure. I am talking about rotational grazing here, not a fenced-in area that you pile a bunch of animals onto and let them stay there for the year or years. We need to mimic nature. Moving our livestock from paddock to paddock keeps us from creating nutrient overload. It also keeps us from having soil compaction issues and allows the pasture plants to regrow and renew that soil. Over time, we have noticed that our pastures are getting better and better. With the increased quality of pasture we see the increased quality in our livestock.

So, if you are thinking about livestock on your farm, consider for what purpose (or purposes) will you have them. Just having them for the added fertility is a huge consideration. But also think about why you wish to have them because they are a big responsibility. They can be expensive if you don't have a plan to feed them from your farm. If you are raising them for a market product, make sure you know your market first. Who is buying them? Where will they be processed? How will you deliver them? In many states, you will be required to have a meat broker's license in order to sell meat, an egg license in order to offer eggs for sale, and you will need to register your bees. Look into all the facets of this livestock venture. Even just having your own eggs, meat, and honey for you and your family is a great reason to have your own farm animals.

BEEKEEPING

Here is another option for livestock on your farm: bees! Yes, bees are considered livestock. We have had two or three hives on the farm for the past dozen years. While we do get a bit of honey and have sold a small amount, we are mostly interested in having bees for the purpose of pollination and for their part in the whole ecosystem. To that end, we have planted about five acres of recreated native prairie grasses and flowers. This acts as a great food source and medicine chest for the bees. Creating that habitat has increased the diversity on the farm and has allowed our bees to stay alive, even when other hives in the area have died out. We don't medicate or feed our bees. We really don't do a lot with them and even allow them to swarm if they want. Even if they swarm and a hive remains empty for a few months, it seems that a scout bee eventually finds the hive again and they move back in. I would encourage you to learn about the amazing life of bees—all kinds of bees— and to create habitat and a home for them on your farm.

Edible flowers are beloved by chefs (and by the rest of us!).

CHAPTER 13

Random Thoughts

Bits and Pieces

Y ou know how sometimes you go through your day thinking about stuff? And sometimes you want to remember some of it for later? This is a collection of those kinds of thoughts that may or may not have fit in any of the other logical places in this book. But I believe they might be helpful to think about as we work on our farm.

The opposite-page photo is a sampler box of edible flowers: squash blossoms, daylily, oregano, hollyhock, coriander, borage, and wild bergamot. Edible flowers are a thing. Many chefs are looking for the eye candy. All of these lend themselves to that. Remember how visual chefs are. Actually, all of us tend toward being more visual characters. Use that to your advantage. Many of the seed catalogs now list a good selection of edible flowers. We feel they are profitable to grow too!

Thinking about visually exciting things. Think about how your farm looks. What kind of condition are the buildings in? How about any of the plantings or landscape? Is your farm clean? Is it inviting? All of these visual images make a difference. Let me show you. Below are a couple pictures of our farm, before I moved back and after.

The big barn in the spring of 1999.

The restored barn in the fall of 2000.

What a difference, right? We as a family did all the work. It was a lot, but really, we only had the material expense out of pocket. When I first moved back to the farm, most of the neighbors kept asking if they could run to town and get us a box of matches! We just kept plugging away at it and were able to get all the buildings restored and looking proud again.

If you can, invite folks to your farm. Host an evening walk and talk. Have homeschool families visit and learn what you are doing. Bring chefs to the farm. They have a ton of questions and ideas. Those conversations are invaluable. Don't be afraid to show and tell. Realize that you can share everything that you know about any subject with someone else, even if they are another farmer, but that doesn't diminish what you still know. It is like giving recipes. You can share a recipe, but seldom do two people come out with the exact same product in the end.

Learn to operate your farm as many days of the year as you can. By that I mean to utilize its full potential. Spread the cash flow out over the whole year. Also spread the workload over the whole year. We begin our season with tapping the maple trees and making maple syrup. That begins in February. Once that is winding down we are into the hoophouses and planting or harvesting crops that have overwintered. Then onto the field crops. Try to schedule your farm year with all of this in mind.

And going along with the above, Joel Salatin and Eliot Coleman always say to find the hidden farm on your farm. Get to know your farm and land intimately. Look for opportunities that may lie hidden. Not that we are mining our farms, but realize there may be possibilities that are there in plain sight that you haven't recognized yet. Learn to identify any wild edibles on your farm. Not everyone has them! There is a market for those as well.

Think about what kind of business model you wish to operate under. We are a LLC, which limits the liability that each of us would be responsible for. Get insurance. While we have never had to use it, one claim could be quite devastating. Try to separate or limit your personal risks from the farm.

Learn to utilize the seeming waste streams from one enterprise onto another. For instance, we bring back all the wheat, rye, and corn screenings from the cleaning mill and feed them to our chickens or use them as cover crop seed in buffer areas. Also, see these nifty vegetable crates? The restaurants save them for us from any of the other purveyors. We have hundreds of them and have never bought a one. We use them for storage of our root and apple crops. We use them to deliver each week to the restaurants. We have used them to dry corn or small squash in. So many uses, and otherwise they would have ended up in the landfill.

Likewise, a few years ago, one of our restaurants asked if we would consider getting a diesel delivery van. They wanted to give us all of their used vegetable oil. Just so happened one of our neighbors had a biodiesel set-up. They could take the used oil we brought back from the restaurants and clean it up and turn it into biodiesel. We ran our delivery van for a couple years on free fuel. We eventually outgrew that van, but it saved us a lot while we had it.

If you are needing more ideas for potential markets, think about a few of these possibilities: workplace CSA, multi-farm CSA,

groceries or co-ops, nursing home or VA medical facilities, school lunch programs, meals on wheels programs, brewers and distillers, private schools and universities, buying clubs or personal chefs and trainers, cooking clubs, create your own home delivery service. And don't forget about taking extras to local food pantries or food banks. Sometimes they have funds to purchase fresh product. But remember them if you have extra that needs to go somewhere. The donations are always appreciated!

When you pack your product for orders or sale, add some extra just to make everyone happy. If you have an order for five pounds of something, add another quarter or half pound. More than likely you have enough to do that, and it matters. If you ever have a customer check the weight, you definitely want to have more rather than less!

Be professional with your invoices. Have something nice looking and that looks like you are in a real business. Be timely with your communications and your deliveries. If you are going to a restaurant, realize when they are busy and serving folks. We try our best to make all our deliveries before the evening service time. Once service starts for them, they really don't want to be accepting more product. They are busy!

Recently I took an online course on improving memory. One concept that I learned has definite crossover in the area of memory and marketing. What I discovered was that we learn and market in three different ways. First is by duration—a lot of ads over a long time or a lot of information that is reviewed for long periods. The second way is by frequency, like radio or online ads that seem to come on every five minutes. That relates also to learning—having the same thing presented in repeat fashion. The third way is intensity. This is the most efficient way we learn or market. We do it through action, association, emotion, imagination, and visualization. In your conversations and in your marketing materials or your actual product, use the intensity model. It works! Try to create connections with at least one or more of those intensity qualities.

Next, read! Learn all you can, every day. There is a lot of information out there. I know that the internet has a lot to potentially offer, and if that is your world, keep reading. I think reading is one of the most important ways that information from those who have done it gets transferred. Hence this book!

After that—and I know I have said it a few times throughout these pages—listen. Don't worry about what you are going to say next. Just listen and be in the moment as people are talking to you. We can learn so many things about what people want if we just hear and listen to them. Learn to file that information somewhere that you can use it later. Learn people's names. These little things can make all the difference in creating the relationships we need to be successful.

And along with that, come to know who you are and then be who you are. You are embarking on an amazing adventure. This experience will change you. It will make you see the world differently and allow you to influence your part of it. Accept this challenge. It is who you are.

I hope this book has been a meaningful guide as you consider your path in farming.

CHAPTER 14

Evaluation Time

Are You Ready Yet?

So, here we are.

How are you doing? Mostly good? Me too, pretty much! We have made it this far, and now we need to make some decisions. Can you do this?

When I decided I wanted to get all of this out of my head, I made a conscious decision not to write a "how to" book, but a guide book. A field guide. There are plenty of "how to" books out there—*How to Grow World Record Tomatoes, How to Grow More Vegetables, How to Farm*—and there are thousands of YouTube videos on how to do everything. What I wanted to share was something different, something more internal, something to help guide you over a similar landscape that we have traveled. I hope I have done that. I hope you have found this helpful and motivating. But having said that, it is still just a guide. It is not a map to success. There are many paths to a destination. Only you and/or your family can make the decisions that are best for you. Choose wisely! Also, remember that there is a reason they still put erasers on pencils. If you are going to make mistakes, and you will, try to make small ones and not the same mistake too many times. Just learn to fail a bit better. Learn to learn from those setbacks. The lessons are there. Listen intently!

I hope you will use this book, even in the field. The section on plant health is meant to be functional. It is meant to help answer questions that you have as you walk through your crops. It will help you to see what you are looking at. The resource section has a myriad of links and potential sources for continued learning. Spend some time there. I know they have been helpful to us.

So, who do you want to be? What do you want to do? Has your vision or understanding of what you have dreamed about changed? Do you still have questions? That is good—keep asking questions and seeking answers.

Do you have more confidence in your decisions? Something I hope you do is to begin eliminating any automatic negative talk. When you say, "Oh, I'm not good at talking to people," I want you to add the word "yet." If you think you aren't good at driving a tractor in a straight line, remember to say "yet!" You can do it. Go back and evaluate all of your ideas, plans, dreams, and visions. Be critical in your thoughts and figure out what pieces of this you are solidly comfortable with and what pieces you still need to work on. Remember to begin small. Build this up and add onto your progress. Celebrate the progress and the successes. Share your experiences with folks around you.

Recently we had a number of folks from across North America come to the farm for a two-day learning experience. Some were just beginning and dreaming of their farm. They wanted to know what crops to plant, how to graft trees, what kind of equipment they should purchase, and where to find good seed. Others have been involved in a conventional family operation for some time and were looking to see if there were other opportunities for farming with fewer chemicals and more sustainable practices. Still others were just wanting to be part of something larger than themselves, not necessarily farming; they wanted to understand where good food comes from. This is the community. There were those who expressed their fear of being ridiculed by their neighbors as being weird or too different. There were those who just were on a mission to make this happen. And two folks who wanted to understand how to be better consumers and maybe one day, years from now, create their farm. My point is that there are so many folks looking to be a part of something fantastic. They are looking for a community of like-minded, caring people. This is the tribe we all are seeking. It is up to you and I to be the conduit for helping to make that happen!

Here are my three parting shots:

1. First, decide who you are. Once you figure that out, then deciding what you are going to do is much easier. Decide what kind of farmer you want to be, and then be that person!

2. Second, keep learning, always. Be willing to change with the new knowledge you acquire. Be open to understanding before being understood. That will serve you really well!

3. And finally, begin. Start small, but begin. Quit being a wannabe. We only get one round at this life; do something with purpose and meaning! Several years ago, a friend of mine told me to keep planting until you are planted. I like that a lot. So, if you are ready, we need to get to it, with purpose! Keep planting, and do me a favor: let me know how it goes!

CHAPTER 15

Resources

B elow are some of our favorite resources. They have been extremely useful in our experience. This is by no means a total list of what is available out there, but it's a good start.

SEED AND NURSERY COMPANIES	WEBSITE
Willis Orchards	www.willisorchards.com
Big Horse Creek Farm	www.bighorsecreekfarm.com
Oikos Tree Crops	www.oikostreecrops.com
Dixondale Farms	www.dixondalefarms.com
Daisy Farms	www.daisyfarms.net
Underwood Gardens	www.underwoodgardens.com
Potato Garden	www.potatogarden.com
High Mowing Seeds	www.highmowingseeds.com
Fedco Seeds	www.fedcoseeds.com
Johnny's Seeds	www.johnnyseeds.com
Seed Savers Exchange	www.seedsavers.org
Territorial Seed Company	www.territorialseed.com
Baker Creek Heirloom Seeds	www.rareseeds.com
Adaptive Seed Company	www.adaptiveseeds.com
Uprising Seeds	www.uprisingorganics.com
Kitchen Garden Seeds	www.kitchengardenseeds.com
Seeds from Italy	www.growitalian.com
Chili Peppers	www.www.chileplants.com
Wild Garden Seeds	www.www.wildgardenseed.com

BOOKS AND VIDEOS	WEBSITE
Acres U.S.A.	www.acresusa.com
Small Farmer's Journal	www.smallfarmersjournal.com
Eliot Coleman	www.fourseasonfarm.com
Anne and Eric Nordell	www.youtube.com/watch?v=JJ6GcsStfks
MOSES Organic Conference	www.mosesorganic.org
Sustainable Agriculture, Research and Education	
	www.sustainableagriculture.net
Advancing Eco Ag	www.advancingecoag.com
Attra Sustainable Agriculture	www.attra.ncat.org
Michael Phillips, apple grower	www.herbsandapples.com/orchard
Sustainable Documentary	www. sustainabledocumentary.com
John Ikerd	www.johnikerd.com
Soil testing	www.blinc.com
Sap analysis	www.crophealthlabs.com
Farmer crop info	www.roxburyfarm.com

INFORMATION FOR FARMERS	
Heritage breed livestock	www.livestockconservancy.org
Tractor information	www.www.tractordata.com
Farm hacks	www.farmhack.org/tools

Exchange capacity	20-28
PH	6.4-6.8
Organic Matter	4.0-5.0
Estimated nitrogen release	100
Soluble sulfur	30
Phosphorus – mehlich III	300
Phosphorus – bray II	400
Potassium exchange cations	500
Calcium – base %	68-72%
Magnesium	13-15%
Potassium	3-5%
Sodium	0.50%
Other bases	4-5%
Hydrogen	7-10%

MINORS

Boron ppm	1
Iron	100-200
Manganese	40-60
Copper	3
Zinc	4
Aluminum	less than 800

Acknowledgements

Getting to this point of unpacking my experiences and the information stored in my head comes with an acknowledgement of so many friends and family who have helped to make this a reality.

First, we are so blessed to be able to continue to work the land that our ancestors settled on and to be in the line of descendants who have taken their turn. To all of them and to my mom, I am grateful for this opportunity.

Next, this is mostly Kris's fault! She dreamed, encouraged, and continues to support this amazing endeavor. We owe her a big helping of gratitude!

Will and Katie and their new family are the next in line and I couldn't be more proud. The farm is in great hands.

Much of the idea for this book also comes from trying to leverage the incredible exposure and questions we received following the release of the documentary *Sustainable*. Thank you, Matt and Annie, for shining your light on us and allowing us to be seen by so many people around the world.

Gary Reding and Carol Richmond were instrumental in keeping me encouraged and focused. Their expertise, proofing, and edits, were able to provide context, content, and valuable insight as to what this book could be. Gary's information and photos of plant and soil health are critical in understanding what we do. Our weekend of fireside chats will always be with me!

Jody Eddy, author and friend, has been a huge cheerleader. As have so many of our chef friends, Greg and Chris among them. I am most grateful for all of them.

Bob Boehle, a long-time friend who served as my grandfather's crop consultant, has continued to provide inspiration and insight!

To Ryan and the Acres U.S.A. staff—thank you for this opportunity to have a platform to share all of this. Your continued commitment to providing information and a forum for all who are interested in taking care of this land and its inhabitants is to be commended!

And finally, you the reader. Thank you for allowing me to have this conversation with you. It has been a good one, and one that I trust will serve us both very well.

Index

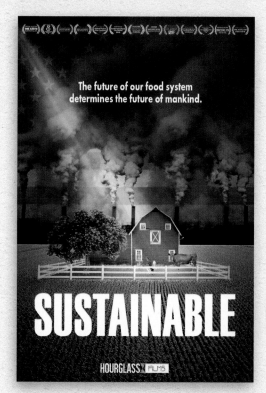

Sustainable

A vital investigation of the economic and environmental instability of America's food system, from the agricultural issues we face — soil loss, water depletion, climate change, pesticide use — to the community of leaders who are determined to fix it. Sustainable is a film about the land, the people who work it and what must be done to sustain it for future generations.

The narrative of the film focuses on Marty Travis, the author of this book, a seventh-generation farmer in central Illinois who watched his land and community fall victim to the pressures of big agribusiness. Determined to create a proud legacy for his son, Marty transforms his profitless wasteland and pioneers the sustainable food movement in Chicago.

Sustainable travels the country seeking leadership and wisdom from some of the most forward thinking farmers like Bill Niman, Klaas Martens and John Kempf—heroes who challenge the ethical decisions behind industrial agriculture. It is a story of hope and transformation, about passion for the land and a promise that it can be restored to once again sustain us.

About the Filmmakers:

Matt Wechsler and Annie Speicher are the storytellers at Hourglass Films behind "Sustainable". The film is a passion project for them, combining their roles as food activists with their talents as documentary filmmakers. "Sustainable" was screened at 20+ film festivals around the world and recently won the 2016 Accolade Global Humanitarian Award for Outstanding Achievement. Their past work includes the 2012 New York Emmy-nominated documentary "Different is the New Normal", which aired nationally on PBS and was narrated by Michael J. Fox. They are currently working on a new film called "Right to Harm" about the health effects of factory farming on rural Americans. The film is set to premiere in 2018.

DVD • 92 minutes • $19.95 • Copyright 2017

More Books from Acres U.S.A.

Order by calling 1-800-355-5313, or online at www.acresusa.com. Also, enjoy our free informational articles from many of our popular authors at www.ecofarmingdaily.com.

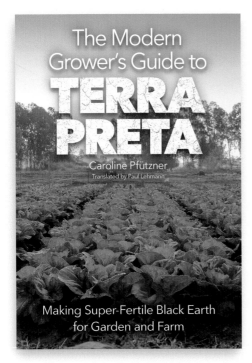

Terra Preta
by Caroline Pfützner

Translated into English for the first time, author Caroline Pfützner introduces us to terra preta, or black earth of the Amazon, what is considered the most fertile soil in the world. Rightly so, because this ultra-rich, living material literally builds a permanent humus layer on the land. The true results of working with this almost miraculous substance are healthy plants and a rich harvest — without outside fertilizer inputs.

And even better, widespread use of terra preta would actively protect the climate. This practical book by a world authority on the subject—available in English for the first time—practically guarantees success in production and application of terra preta whether in the garden, raised beds, larger growing operations, or simple balcony boxes. Practical examples from commercial-scale agriculture illustrate the true potential of terra preta.

Making black earth by yourself. Learn step-by-step how to make top-quality terra preta yourself.

Using terra preta in your garden or farm. See how the author grows healthy, bountiful crops organically without synthetic fertilizer.

Practical in the extreme. Far from a cumbersome scientific text, benefit from the rich, practical experience of the author.

Extensive background knowledge. Understand the deeper story—historical and scientific—of terra preta and its implications for modern times.

#7566 • Softcover • 176 pages • Copyright 2019 • $28.00

The Farm as Ecosystem

by Jerry Brunetti

In The Farm as Ecosystem, natural product formulator and farm consultant Jerry Brunetti brings together a wealth of education and uncanny observations in this probing volume on the interconnected dynamics of the farm — geology, biology, and diversity of life. Learn to look at — and manage — your farm very differently by gaining a deeper understanding of the complementary roles of all facets of your farm.

With this unique perspective, the author guides the reader on a journey through the modern farm as an ecosystem, providing intimate anecdotes and comprehensive details that appreciate all dimensions of the farm. Brunetti's work is invaluable to the contemporary farmer and to those seeking an original appraisal of farming and its future.

Topics covered by The Farm as Ecosystem include:
- The physical, chemical and biological aspects of soil;
- Understanding compost and compost tea;
- Working with foliar nutrition;
- The roles of trace elements in farming;
- Water and your farm;
- Cover cropping systems . . . and more.

The book eco-farmers everywhere have been waiting for is here.

Copyright 2013 • Softcover • 352 pages • $30.00

About Jerry Brunetti

JERRY BRUNETTI, 1950-2014, worked as a soil and crop consultant, primarily for livestock farms and ranches, and improved crop quality and livestock performance and health on certified organic farms. In 1979, he founded Agri-Dynamics Inc., and confounded Earthworks in 1990. He spoke widely on the topics of human, animal and farm health

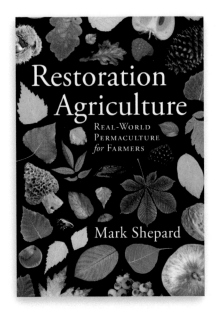

Restoration Agriculture
by Mark Shepard

Around the globe most people get their calories from "annual" agriculture—plants that grow fast for one season, produce lots of seeds, then die. Every single human society that has relied on annual crops for staple foods has collapsed. Restoration Agriculture explains how we can have all of the benefits of natural, perennial ecosystems and create agricultural systems that imitate nature in form and function while still providing for our food, building, fuel and many other needs—in your own backyard, farm or ranch. This book, based on real-world practices, presents an alternative to the agriculture system of eradication and offers exciting hope for our future.

Copyright 2013 • Softcover • 339 pages • $30.00

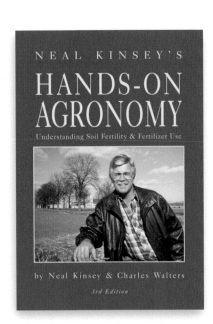

Hands-On Agronomy
by Neal Kinsey

The soil is more than just a substrate that anchors crops in place. An ecologically balanced soil system is essential for maintaining healthy crops. Hands-On Agronomy is a comprehensive manual on effective soil fertility management providing many on-farm examples to illustrate the various principles and how to use them. The function of micronutrients, earthworms, soil drainage, tilth, soil structure, and organic matter is explained in thorough detail.

Neal Kinsey demonstrates that working with the soil produces healthier crops with a higher yield. To that end, he provides an understanding of eco-agriculture as a viable enterprise that is both naturally and commercially sustainable. This work offers advice that is both highly valuable and applicable to the farmer of any level and promotes an ecological understanding of the farm from the ground up.

Copyright 2013,1993 • Softcover • 391 pages • $35.00

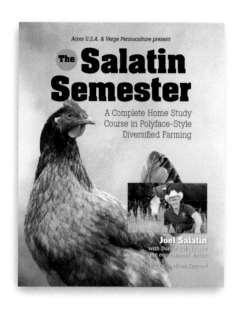

Salatin Semester DVD Set
by Joel Salatin/Verge Permaculture

A Complete Study of How to Run a Farm Like Polyface Farm

What happens when trailblazing urban agro-ecologists Rob and Michelle Avis of Verge Permaculture host superstar "lunatic farmer" Joel Salatin for a three-day, three-workshop weekend...then expand and enhance that recorded wisdom in a three-month online intensive? You get an encyclopedic compendium of small-farming entrepreneurial know-how!

And now we've gathered up and distilled every mind-bending morsel of Joel's mob-stocking sagacity from those online events, and captured it all in one encyclopedic extravaganza of integrated agro-education...

...to inspire, inform, and incite you to outrageous small-farming success...forever!

Don't put off this opportunity to own this all-inclusive, no-holds-barred, home study course...whether you're still dreaming of your entrepreneurial farming enterprise, or you're building on the foundations you've already laid, this is the novice-to-guru reference you'll turn to again and again!

Here, Joel Salatin shares decades of hard-learned lessons and advice. Learn about:
- Pastured broilers
- Pastured layers (feathernets & eggmobiles)
- Salad bar beef
- Pigaerator pork
- Irrigation & fencing
- On-farm processing
- Relationship marketing
- Multi-use infrastructure
- Ideal farm layout
- Leasing farms & adding subcontractors

Learn the practical details behind the day-to-day running of Polyface Farm.

18 hours of video on 12 DVDs • 6 hours of audio Q&A • Digital slideshow farm tour • 256-page guidebook •Hardboard shelf box/binder • $249.00